A WORDSWORTH

JET
FIGHTERS

Wordsworth Editions

First published in England 1993 by
Wordsworth Editions Ltd
Cumberland House
Crib Street
Ware
Hertfordshire SG12 9ET

ISBN 1 85326 984 0

Photographs by courtesy of TRH Pictures, London

Cover: a Dassault-Breguet Rafale-A
Right: F-15s of the Alaskan Air Command's
21st Tactical Fighter Wing

Set in 8½/9pt Monophoto Univers
Text conversion and pagination by
August Filmsetting, St Helens

Printed in Italy by Amadeus s.p.a.

Contents

Fairchild Republic F105s

Introduction

The jet engine was invented by Frank Whittle in 1930, but the first turbojet-powered aircraft, the Heinkel 178, was German-made. Designed by Hans von Ohain and piloted by Captain Erich Worsitz, the He 178 first flew on 27 August 1939.

The first production jet fighter was also German, the Messerschmitt Me 262. This was powered by two Junkers Jumo 004 turbojets, and capable of a top speed of 864km/h (540mph); it first flew on 18 June 1942.

The first British-built jet, based on Whittle's design, was the Gloster Meteor, and first flew in March 1943, ten months ahead of the Lockheed F-80 Shooting Star, North America's first jet.

Although the modern jet fighter was born during World War II, there were no actual dogfights between the jet-powered aircraft. The Shooting Stars never came to Europe, and the much slower Meteors shot down the V-rockets (flying bombs) over southern England, the Messerschmitts recording the first 'kill', albeit against prop fighters, being used almost exclusively against American daylight bombers.

Following World War II, the jet fighters were developed to go faster, and using an experimental aircraft, the US Air Forces X-1, the sound barrier was finally broken on 14 October 1947 by Major Charles 'Chuck' Yeager. The X-1 had been

The first jet fighter, the
8 *Messerschmitt Me262*

dropped from a B-29 bomber from 6,096m (20,000ft), and the lessons learnt enabled better jet fighters to be developed.

Korea became the next theatre of war, when on 25 June 1950, the communist government of North Korea launched an all-out offensive across the 39th Parallel. North Korea entered the war with Yak-7s and Yak-9s, both ageing piston-engined fighters. America came to South Korea's aid with F-51 Mustangs, also piston-engined, and F-80C Shooting Stars, one of which on 27 June 1950 became the first American jet fighter to register a 'kill', when Captain Raymond Schiller-eff shot down an Ilyushin Il-10 Shturmovik. The build-up in Korea intensified with the despatch of an American carrier-based Grumman F-9F Panther aircraft, and in 1951 the Douglas F3D Skynight. Major William Stratton and Master Sergeant Hans Hoglind of the US Marine Corps, flying their F3D, became the first to make a night 'kill' by one jet against another on 3 November 1952 by bringing down a Yak-15 'Feather'.

However, the first real dogfight between jet fighters took place on 8 November 1951, when a flight of six Soviet MiG-15 'Fagots' engaged F-80C Shooting Stars, which were flying escort to B-29s on a raid over North Korea, and Lieutenant Russell Brown became the first jet pilot in history to shoot down an enemy jet in combat.

The North American F-86 Sabres then flew over 75,000 sorties in Korea, amassing over 750 'kills' against the MiG-15s. Korea confirmed that the training and attitude of the fighter pilot were as important as the aircraft's technology.

The Sabres were followed into battle in 1953 by the Super Sabres, the world's first fighters capable of sustaining level speeds greater than Mach 1. Named after the Austrian scientist Ernst Mach, Mach 1 is the speed of sound, which at sea level is 1,216km/h (760mph) and which decreases steadily with altitude as the atmosphere thins and cools, so that at 10,970m (36,000ft) Mach 1 is equal to 1,054km/h (659mph).

The Super Sabres were followed five months later by the Convair F-102 Delta Dagger, a delta-wing design fighter built with its own integrated weapons system with its own missiles.

In answer to the American developments during the time of the Korean War, the Russians developed the MiG-15 into the MiG-17 'Fresco', followed by the MiG-19 'Farmer', which was eventually exported to over 20 other countries and was copied by the Chinese, without a licence, in the Shenyang F-6. The MiG-21 'Fishbed' entered service in 1959, since when over 10,000 have been built. Including the Chinese F-7 copy it remains in service with over 40 airforces.

From the end of World War II to the mid-1950s,

over 20 new fighters came into service, but development costs combined with the easing of political pressures slowed development to only six during the following decade. Independent states had tripled since World War II, and all of these new countries wanted airforces, making new markets available.

The British-built Hawker Hunter in its various versions was sold to 12 countries, and production totalled 1,900 units. The small, light Folland Gnat was purposely designed as a cheap fighter/trainer for these developing countries, while the Northrop F-5A Freedom Fighter was successfully exported to over 20 countries, before the F-5E Tiger II upgraded version appeared.

French development had started in 1949 with the Dassault-Breguet M.D.450 Ouragan, followed by the swept-wing Mystère II, the Improved Mystère IV, and the supersonic Super Mystère. By 1956, the Mirage III prototype had flown. Israel ordered Mirage III variants, which became the Mirage 5, and between them, these were exported to a further 20 countries. Other worthy 1950s developments were the Saab J 35 Draken, years ahead of its time, and the BAe Lightning.

In 1963, McDonnell Douglas produced what was the most outstanding multi-role combat

Designed in the 1950s: Dassault's Mystère IVA strike fighters, powered
by Hispano-Suiza Verdun turbojets

plane yet produced, the F-4 Phantom II. Big and heavy, the two seat Phantom was designed for any role, from carrier or land base. Its weapons load of eight missiles, good radar and reliability made it a winner with the US Navy, Marines and Air Force, and the airforces of 11 other nations.

The F-4 Phantoms, together with F-8 Crusaders, flew the first US Navy carrier missions in the Vietnam War, but in dogfights between these and the MiG-21s, the American aircrafts' superiority was not decisive. Investigations concluded that the pilots were insufficiently trained in dogfighting, airborne tactics and combat precautions and in 1969 the Navy established a postgraduate course later known as Top Gun. With the 1972 resumption of bombing Vietnam, American pilots achieved a 'kill' ratio of 8:1; in 1975, USAF established its 'Top Gun' Red Flag programme.

At 8.45am local time on 5 June 1967, aircraft of the Israeli Air Force flying at very low level hit nine major Egyptian airbases; their attacks lasted ten minutes before they returned to base, making way for the next wave of attack. By midday, they had destroyed 250 aircraft at 13 airfields, and in the afternoon they struck again, this time at five Syrian and two Jordanian airfields. The war lasted just six days; in all, 390 Arab aircraft were destroyed, the Israelis lost 32, and on the first day some IAF pilots registered eight sorties.

In the last quarter of a century, the advances in computer technology have had a profound effect on the fighter aircraft. The cutting edge of flight technology has moved from fast jets to rockets, and the development of the SAM both robbed the fighter of its main reason for existence and provided a revolution in aircraft combat, introducing radar warning receivers to detect incoming missiles and electronic countermeasures equipment to distract the missiles, in what became known as Wild Weasel technology. This was to be proven in the Yom Kippur War of 1973.

The McDonnell Douglas F-15 Eagle, which entered service in 1974, carries more than 909kg (2,000lb) of electronics in addition to its M61 Vulcan gun and eight missiles. A computerised head-up display informs the pilot of his speed, position and his direction, together with any threats, and the responses available to him. The Hughes APG-63 pulse-Doppler radar is capable of engaging targets at 192km (120 miles).

The use of lightweight composites, maximum speeds in excess of Mach 2, supersonic capability at sea level, head-up displays, fly-by-wire controls and terrain-following radar by today's pilots represents the latest technology being pushed to its absolute limits; a far cry from what was available in the last days of World War II, 50 years ago.

F-15As of the 49th TFW, Holloman
AFB, caught mirrored by rainwater

Aeritalia G91Y

Country of origin: Italy
Type: tactical strike and reconnaissance fighter
First flight: December 1966
Accommodation: pilot seated on a Martin-Baker ejector seat
Armament (fixed): two 33mm DEFA 552 cannon with 125 rounds per gun
Armament (disposable): up to 1,814kg (4,000lb) carried on four hardpoints
Electronics and operational equipment: communication and navigation equipment
Powerplant and fuel system: two 1,850kg (4,080lb) afterburning thrust General Electric J85-GE-13As; total internal fuel capacity of 3,200 litres (704 Imp gal)
Performance: maximum speed 1,140km/h (708mph); service ceiling 12,500m (41,010ft); range 385km (240 miles)
Weights: empty 3,682kg (8,117lb); normal take-off 7,800kg (17,196lb); maximum take-off 8,700kg (19,180lb)
Dimensions: span 9.01m (29ft 6.5in); length 11.67m (38ft 3.5in); height 4.43m (14ft 6.5in); wing area 18.13m² (195.15sq ft)
Production: 77 aircraft

The G91Y was produced in limited quantities for the German and Italian air forces

Aeritalia/Aermacchi/EMBRAER (AMX International) AM-X

Country of origin: Italy/Brazil
Type: close air support
First flight: August 1989
Accommodation: pilot on ejector seat
Armament (fixed): one 20mm M61A1 Vulcan six-barrel rotary cannon with 350 rounds or (Brazilian aircraft) two 30mm DEFA 554 cannon with 125 rounds per gun
Armament (disposable): carried on seven hardpoints up to a weight of 3,800kg (7,377lb)
Electronics and operational equipment: communications and navigation equipment, plus Fiat Pointer ranging radar
Powerplant and fuel system: one 5,000kg (11,023lb) thrust Alfa Romeo Avio/Fiat/Piaggio-built Rolls-Royce Spey Mk 807 non-afterburning turbofan and a total internal fuel capacity of 3,555 litres (782 Imp gal)
Performance: maximum speed 1,163 km/h (723mph); service ceiling 13,000m (42,650ft); radius 520km (323 miles) with warload
Weights: empty 6,700kg (14,771lb); maximum take-off 12,500kg (27,557lb)
Dimensions: span 10.0m (32ft 9.75in); length 13.575m (44ft 6.4in); height 4.576m (15ft 0.25in); wing area 21m² (226.04sq ft)
Production: Italy 187 (AMX) + 51 (AMX-T); Brazil 64 + 15

An Italian Air Force AM-X, fitted
with two Sea Killer missiles

Aero Vodochody L-39D Albatros

Country of origin: Czechoslovakia
Type: single-seat light attack aircraft
First flight: November 1968
Accommodation: pilot on ejector seat
Armament (fixed): a pod containing one two-barrel GSh-23 23mm cannon and between 150 and 180 rounds may be attached under the fuselage, used with an ASP-3-NMU-39 gunsight
Armament (disposable): a maximum of 1,100kg (2,425lb) of stores
Electronics and operational equipment: communications and navigation equipment
Powerplant and fuel system: one 1,720kg (3,792lb) thrust Walter Titan turbofan (licence-built Ivchenko AI-25-TL) or a 1,900kg (4,188lb) thrust
Performance: maximum speed with stores 630km/h (391mph) at 6,000m (19,685ft); range 780km (485 miles) with stores, and 1,600km (994 miles) for ferrying
Weights: empty 3,330kg (7,341lb); normal take-off 4,570kg (10,075lb); maximum take-off 5,270kg (11,618lb)
Dimensions: span 9.46m (31ft 0.5in); length 12.32m (40ft 5in); height 4.72m (15ft 5.5in); wing area 18.80m² (202.36sq ft)

This Czechoslovakian-built aircraft is also produced in a two-seat trainer version for the Czechoslovakian Air Force

Atlas Aircraft Corporation Cheetah D

Country of origin: South Africa
Type: multi-role fighter
Operational: July 1987
Accommodation: pilot
Armament (fixed): two 30mm cannon
Armament (disposable): up to 5,775kg (12,731lb)
Electronics and operational equipment: integrated nav/attack system with a laser designator, a chaff/flare dispenser and dual-role Elta EL/M-200 1B radar
Powerplant and fuel system: one SNECMA Atar 9K-50 afterburning turbojet, rated at 70.6kN (15,873lb) thrust
Performance: maximum speed 2,350km/h (1,460mph); service ceiling 17,000m (55,775ft); range 768-km (477-mile) radius on a hi-lo-hi mission
Weights: empty 7,285kg (16,060lb); loaded 16,200kg (35,714lb)
Dimensions: span 8.22m (26ft 11.5in); length 15.40m (50ft 6.3in); height 4.55m (14ft 11.25in); wing area 52.67m² (566.95sq ft)

A Cheetah of the South African Air Force

Avro Canada CF-105 Arrow Mk 1

Country of origin: Canada
Type: all-weather, long-range interceptor
First flight: March 1958
Accommodation: pilot and systems operator seated in tandem on ejector seats
Armament (fixed): none
Armament (disposable): six Douglas AIR-2 Genie air-to-air missiles carried internally
Electronics and operational equipment: communications and navigation equipment
Powerplant and fuel system: two 10,699kgp (23,500lb) Pratt & Whitney J75-P turbojets with reheat
Performance: maximum speed 1,297km/h (700kt) or Mach 1.05 at sea level; service ceiling 15.240m (50,000ft); radius 663km (358 naut miles) with 5 minutes at Mach 1.5
Weights: empty 22,211kg (48,923lb), maximum take-off 31,144kg (68,600lb)
Dimensions: span 15.24m (50ft); length 23.71m (77.82ft); wing area 113.8m² (1,225sq ft)
Production: 5 aircraft

Canada scrapped all Mk 1 Arrows, together with the one Mk 2, in
February 1959

British Aerospace Harrier GR.Mk 3

Country of origin: UK
Type: V/STOL close-support and recce
First flight: prototype October 1960
Accommodation: pilot
Armament (fixed): (optional) two Aden 30mm cannon with 100 rounds per gun
Armament (disposable): up to a maximum cleared weight of 2,268kg (5,000lb)
Electronics and operational equipment: communication and navigation equipment, plus Ferranti FE 541 inertial navigation and attack system, Smiths head-up display, and Ferranti Type 106 laser-ranger and marked-target seeker
Powerplant and fuel system: one 9,752kg (21,500lb) thrust Rolls-Royce (Bristol) Pegasus Mk 103 vectored-thrust turbofan
Performance: maximum speed over 1,186km/h (737mph) at low altitude; service ceiling more than 15,240m (50,000ft); range 667-km (414-mile) radius
Weights: empty 5,579kg (12,300lb) with pilot; maximum take-off over 11,340kg (25,000lb)
Dimensions: span 7.70m (25ft 3in), or 9.04m (29ft 8in) with low-drag ferry tips; length 14.27m (46ft 10in); height 3.45m (11ft 4in); wing area 18.68m² (201.1sq ft), or 20.07m² (216sq ft) with ferry tips

The Mk 3 has a revised nose, accommodating a laser ranger and marked-target seeker

British Aerospace Hawk 200

Country of origin: UK
Type: multi-role combat aircraft
First flight: April 1987
Accommodation: pilot
Armament (fixed): one or two 25mm Aden cannon and 100 rounds per gun in a lower fuselage installation
Armament (disposable): carried on a maximum of five hardpoints up to a maximum of 3,493kg (7,700lb)
Electronics and operational equipment: communications and navigation equipment plus a Ferranti F195 sight and optional radar
Powerplant and fuel system: one 2,651kg (5,845lb) thrust Rolls-Royce/Turboméca Adour Mk 871 non-afterburning turbofan
Performance: maximum speed 1,038km/h (645mpg) at sea level; initial climb rate 5,221m (11,510ft) per minute; service ceiling 15,240m (50,000ft); radius 617km (383 miles) on a hi-lo-hi mission
Weights: empty 4,128kg (9,100lb); maximum take-off 9,101kg (20,065lb)
Dimensions: span 9.39m (30ft 9.75in); length 11.17m (36ft 7.75in); height 3.99m (13ft 1.25in); wing area 16.69m² (179.6sq ft)
Production: 20 aircraft

The only all-British military aircraft being built

British Aerospace Hunter FGA.Mk 9

Country of origin: UK
Type: fighter and weapons-training aircraft
First flight: July 1951
Accommodation: pilot
Armament (fixed): four Aden 30mm cannon with 135 rounds per gun in a detachable ventral pack
Armament (disposable): typical underwing stores are 454kg (1,000lb) bombs plus 227kg (500lb) bombs
Electronics and operational equipment: communication and navigation equipment, plus ranging radar
Powerplant and fuel system: one 4,604kg (10,150lb) thrust Rolls-Royce RA.28 Avon Mk 207
Performance: maximum speed 978km/h (620mph) at high altitude; range 2,965km (1,840 miles) with two 1,046-litre (230-Imp gal) drop-tanks
Weights: empty 5,901kg (13,010lb); normal take-off 8,165kg (18,000lb); maximum take-off 10,886kg (24,000lb) with two 456-litre (100-Imp gal) and two 1,046-litre (230-Imp gal) drop-tanks
Dimensions: span 10.25m (33ft 8in); length 13.98m (45ft 10.5in); height 4.02m (13ft 2in); wing area 32.42m² (349sq ft)

The Mk 9 was the definitive postwar
UK ground-attack fighter

British Aerospace Lightning F.Mk 6

Country of origin: UK
Type: interceptor fighter
First flight: April 1957
Accommodation: pilot seated on a Martin-Baker ejector seat
Armament (fixed): two Aden 30mm cannon with 120 rounds per gun in the front portion of the ventral fuel tank
Armament (disposable): up to 144 rockets or six 454kg (1,000lb) HE bombs
Electronics and operational equipment: communication and navigation equipment, plus Ferranti Airpass AI-23S interception radar
Powerplant and fuel system: two 7,420kg (16,360lb) afterburning thrust Rolls-Royce Avon Mk 301 turbojets
Performance: maximum speed 2,112km/h (1,320mph) or Mach 2 at 10,970m (36,000ft); climb to 12,190m (40,000ft) in 2 minutes 30 seconds; service ceiling 16,765m (55,000ft); range 1,287km (800 miles) on internal fuel
Weights: empty 12,717kg (28,041lb); maximum take-off 19,047kg (42,000lb)
Dimensions: span 10.62m (34ft 10in); length 16.84m (55ft 3in) including probe; height 5.97m (19ft 7in); wing area 42.97m² (458.5sq ft)

British Aerospace Sea Harrier FRS.Mk 1

Country of origin: UK
Type: carrierborne STOVL fighter
First flight: October 1960
Entered service: 1981
Accommodation: pilot on a Martin-Baker Mk 10H zero/zero ejector seat
Armament (fixed): two 30mm Aden Mk 4 cannon with 150 rounds per gun
Armament (disposable): carried on five hardpoints up to a maximum weight of 2,268kg (5,000lb)
Electronics and operational equipment: communications and navigation equipment
Powerplant and fuel system: one 9,752kg (21,500lb) thrust Rolls-Royce Pegasus Mk 104 vectored-thrust non-afterburning turbofan; internal fuel capacity 2,865 litres (630 Imp gal)
Performance: maximum speed 1,110km/h (690mph) or Mach 0.9 at sea level; initial climb rate about 15,240m (50,000ft) per minute; service ceiling 15,545m (51,000ft); radius 740km (460 miles) with full load
Weights: empty 6,374kg (14,052lb); maximum take-off 11,884kg (26,200lb)
Dimensions: span 7.70m (25ft 3in); length 14.50m (47ft 7in); height 3.71m (12ft 2in); wing area 18.68m² (201.1sq ft)
Production: 80 aircraft

A Sea Harrier of the Indian Navy

Chengdu Aircraft Corp F-7M Airguard

Country of origin: China
Type: interceptor fighter
First flight: 1980
Accommodation: pilot
Armament (fixed): two 30mm Type 30-1 cannon with 60 rounds per gun
Armament (disposable): carried on four hardpoints each rated at 250kg (551lb)
Electronics and operational equipment: communications and navigation equipment; Type 226 ranging radar; Type 956 HUD and weapon-aiming computer system
Powerplant and fuel system: one 6,100kg (13,448lb) afterburning thrust Chengdu Wopen-7B(BM) turbojet and a maximum internal fuel capacity of 2,385 litres (525 Imp gal)
Performance: maximum speed 2,180km/h (1,355mph) or Mach 2.05 at high altitude; initial climb rate 10,800m (35,433ft) per minute; service ceiling 18,200m (59,710ft); radius 600km (373 miles) on a hi-lo-hi mission
Weights: empty 5,275kg (11,629lb); maximum take-off 8,900kg (19,621lb)
Dimensions: span 7.154m (23ft 5.6in); length 13.945m (45ft 9in); height 4.103m (13ft 5.5in); wing area 23.00m² (247.6sq ft)
Production: 583 aircraft

The Chinese-built copy of the MiG-21 series, initially based on the MiG-21F 'Fishbed-C' day interceptor

Convair F-106A Delta Dart

Country of origin: USA
Type: interceptor fighter
First flight: December 1958
Accommodation: pilot
Armament (fixed): one General Electric M61A-1 Vulcan 20mm rotary-barrel cannon
Armament (disposable): one Douglas AIR-2A Genie or AIR-2B Super Genie nuclear-warhead air-to-air rocket plus two or four Hughes AIM-4F or AIM-4G Super Falcon air-to-air missiles
Electronics and operational equipment: communication and navigation equipment, plus Hughes MA-1 interception and fire-control system tied in by data-link to the SAGE (Semi-Automatic Ground Environment) system
Powerplant and fuel system: one 11,113kg (24,500lb) afterburning thrust Pratt & Whitney
Performance: maximum speed 2,455km/h (1,525mph); initial climb rate about 9,145m (30,000ft) per minute; service ceiling 17,325m (57,000ft); range 1,850km (1,150 miles)
Weights: empty 10,726kh (23,646lb); maximum take-off 17,554kg (38,700lb)
Dimensions: span 11.67m (38ft 3.5in); length 21.56m (70ft 8.75in); height 6.18m (20ft 3.25in); wing area 58.65m² (631.3sq ft)

The Delta Dart and the F-102 Delta Dagger were designed for the air-defence of continental USA

40

Dassault-Breguet Etendard IVM

Country of origin: France
Type: shipboard strike aircraft
Accommodation: pilot
Armament (fixed): two DEFA 30mm cannon with 125 rounds per gun
Armament (disposable): this is carried on four underwing hardpoints up to a weight of 1,360kg (3,000lb)
Electronics and operational equipment: communication and navigation equipment, plus Electronique Marcel Dassault Aida ranging radar
Powerplant and fuel system: one 4,400kg (9,700lb) thrust SNECMA Atar 08B turbojet and a total internal fuel capacity of 3,300 litres (726 Imp gal) in wing and fuselage tanks, plus provision for two 600-litre (132-Imp gal) drop-tanks; inflight-refuelling capability
Performance: maximum speed 1,100km/h (684mph); initial climb rate 6,000m (19,685ft) per minute; service ceiling 15,000m (49,215ft); range 1,600km (994 miles) with external weapons
Weights: empty 6,125kg (13,503lb); normal take-off 8,170kg (18,011lb);maximum take-off 10,275kg (22,652lb)
Dimensions: span 9.60m (31ft 5.75in); length 14.40m (47ft 3in); height 4.26m (14ft); wing area 29.0m² (312.16sq ft)

The French Navy's erstwhile attack fighter now serves only as a trainer

Dassault-Breguet Super Etendard

Country of origin: France
Type: carrier-based strike fighter
First flight: June 1978
Accommodation: pilot
Armament (fixed): two DEFA 30mm cannon, plus up to 2,100kg (4,630lb) bombload
Electronics and operational equipment: communication and navigation equipment, plus Thomson-CSF/ESD Agave lightweight multi-function radar, Sagem-Kearfott ETNA inertial platform, Thomson-CSV VE-120 head-up display, air-data computer and navigation display and armament control system
Powerplant and fuel system: one 5,000kg (11,023lb) thrust SNECMA Atar 8K-50 turbojet
Performance: maximum speed about 1,065km/h (662mph); initial climb rate 6,000m (19,685ft) per minute; service ceiling 13,700m (44,950ft); range 850-km (528-mile) radius with AM.39 Exocet missile
Weights: empty 6,500kg (14,330lb); normal take-off 9,450kg (20,835lb); maximum take-off 12,000kg (26,455lb)
Dimensions: span 9.6m (31ft 6in); length 14.31m (46ft 11.5in); height 3.86m (12ft 8in); wing area 24.8m² (267sq ft)
Production: 85 aircraft

The updated version of the Etendard, of which 71 were produced for the Aéronavale

Dassault-Breguet Mirage F.1C

Country of origin: France
Type: multi-role fighter and attack aircraft
First flight: December 1966
Accommodation: pilot
Armament (fixed): two DEFA 553 30mm cannon with 135 rounds per gun
Armament (disposable): this is carried on one under-fuselage, four underwing and two wingtip hardpoints, up to a weight of 4,000kg (8,818lb)
Electronics and operational equipment: communication and navigation equipment, plus Thomson-CSF Cyrano IV fire-control radar
Powerplant and fuel system: one 7,200kg (15,873lb) afterburning thrust SNECMA Atar 9K-50 turbojet
Performance: maximum speed 2,350km/h (1,460mph); initial climb rate 12,780m (41,930ft) per minute; service ceiling 20,000m (65,615ft); range 600-km (373-mile) radius
Weights: empty 7,400kg (16,314lb); normal take-off 10,900kg (24,030lb); maximum take-off 16,200kg (35,714lb)
Dimensions: span 8.40m (27ft 6.75in); length 15m (49ft 2.5in); wing area 25m² (269.1sq ft)
Production: 754 aircraft

The Mirage F.1C, successor to the
46 *Mirage III/5 family*

Dassault-Breguet Mirage IIIE

Country of origin: France
Type: fighter-bomber
First flight: November 1956
Accommodation: pilot seated on a Hispano-built Martin-Baker RM4 ejector seat
Armament (fixed): two DEFA 552A 30mm cannon with 125 rounds per gun
Armament (disposable): up to a maximum of about 2,270kg (5,000lb)
Electronics and operational equipment: communication and navigation equipment, plus fire-control radar (air-to-air and air-to-surface), sighting system and Doppler radar
Powerplant and fuel system: one 6,200kg (13,670lb) afterburning thrust SNECMA Atar 9C
Performance: maximum speed clean 2,350km/h (1,460mph) or Mach 2.2 at 12,000m (39,370ft); service ceiling 17,000m (55,775ft) without rocket motor; range 1,200km (745 miles)
Weights: empty 7,050kg (15,540lb); normal take-off 9,600kg 21,165lb); maximum take-off 13,700kg (30,200lb)
Dimensions: span 8.22m (26ft 11.5in); length 15.03m (49ft 3.5in); height 4.50m (14ft 9in); wing area 35m² (376.75sq ft)

A Mirage III of the Royal Australian Air Force: the most commercially-successful fighter ever built

48

Dassault-Breguet Mirage 5A

Country of origin: France
Type: ground-attack aircraft and interceptor
First flight: May 1967
Accommodation: pilot
Armament (fixed): two DEFA 552A 30mm cannon with 125 rounds per gun
Armament (disposable): this is carried on one underfuselage hardpoint and six underwing hardpoints, to a maximum of more than 4,000kg (8,818lb) with the use of multiple launchers
Electronics and operational equipment: communication and navigation equipment, including an inertial navigation system
Powerplant and fuel system: one 6,200kg (13,670lb) afterburning thrust SNECMA Atar 9C turbojet
Performance: maximum speed clean 2,350km/h (1,460mph) or Mach 2.2 at 12,000m (39,370ft); climb to 11,000m (36,090ft) in 3 minutes; service ceiling 17,000m (55,775ft); range 1,300-km (808-mile) hi-lo-hi radius
Weights: empty 6,600kg (14,550lb); normal take-off 9,600kg (21,165lb); maximum take-off 13,700kg (30,200lb)
Dimensions: span 8.22m (26ft 11.5in); length 15.55m (51ft 0.25in); height 4.50m (14ft 9in); wing area 35m² (376.75sq ft)

A Mirage 5D, an upgraded III of the Lebanese Air Force

Dassault-Breguet Mirage 50

Country of origin: France
Type: multi-mission fighter
First flight: May 1967
Accommodation: pilot
Armament (fixed): two DEFA 552A 30mm cannon with 125 rounds per gun
Armament (disposable): this is carried on one under-fuselage hardpoint, rated at 1,180kg (2,600lb), and six underwing hardpoints
Electronics and operational equipment: communication and navigation equipment, plus CSF-ESD Agave radar, Sagem inertial navigation system and Thomson-CSF head-up display
Powerplant and fuel system: one 7,200kg (15,873lb) afterburning thrust SNECMA Atar 9K-50 turbojet; fuel capacity 3,475 litres (764 Imp gal) plus 1,225 litres (269 Imp gal) in drop-tanks
Performance: maximum speed clean 2,350km/h (1,460mph); initial climb rate 11,100m (36,415ft) per minute; service ceiling 18,000m (59,055ft); range 630-km (391-mile) combat radius
Weights: empty 7,150kg (15,765lb); normal take-off 9,900kg (21,825lb); maximum take-off 13,700kg (30,200lb)
Dimensions: span 8.22m (27ft); length 15.56m (51ft 0.5in); height 4.5m (14ft 9in)

Based on the Mirage III, the 50 is
more potent than the Mirage 5

Dassault-Breguet Mirage 2000

Country of origin: France
Type: interceptor and air-superiority fighter
First flight: March 1978
Accommodation: pilot seated on a Martin-Baker F10Q ejector seat
Armament (fixed): two DEFA 554 30mm cannon with 125 rounds per gun
Armament (disposable): this is carried on nine hardpoints, one under the fuselage rated at 1,800kg (3,968lb); four under the wing roots each rated at 400kg (882lb), and four under the wings to a maximum weight of more than 6,000kg (13,228lb)
Powerplant and fuel system: one 9,000kg (19,840lb) SNECMA M53-5 bleed turbojet
Performance: maximum speed more than 2,350km/h (1,460mph) or Mach 2.2 at 12,000m (39,370ft), and 1,110km/h (690mph) or Mach 0.9 at sea level with bombs; initial climb rate more than 18,000m (59,055ft) per minute; service ceiling 20,000m (65,615ft); range more than 1,800km (1,118 miles) with two 1,700-litre (374-Imp gal) drop-tanks
Weights: empty 7,400kg (16,315lb); maximum take-off 16,500kg (36,375lb)
Dimensions: span 9m (26ft 6in); length 14.35m (47ft 1in); wing area 41m² (441.3sq ft)
Production: 560 aircraft

The success of the 2000 is, in part, due to its fly-by-wire controls

Dassault-Breguet Super Mirage 4000

Country of origin: France
Type: multi-role combat aircraft
Accommodation: pilot on ejector seat
Armament (fixed): two 30mm cannon
Armament (disposable): this is carried on 11 hardpoints (one under the fuselage, four under the wing roots, and six under the wings) to a maximum of more than 8,000kg (17,637lb)
Electronics and operational equipment: communication and navigation equipment
Powerplant and fuel system: two 9,700kg (21,385lb) afterburning thrust SNECMA M53-P2 bleed-turbojets, and a total internal fuel capacity of about 11,400 litres (2,508 Imp gal) in fin, fuselage and wing tanks, plus provision for three 2,500-litre (550-Imp gal) drop-tanks (one under the fuselage and two under the wings)
Performance: maximum speed more than 2,450km/h (1,522mph) or Mach 2.3 at 12,000m (39,370ft); initial climb rate 18,300m (60,040ft) per minute; service ceiling 20,000m (65,615ft); range more than 2,000km (1,243 miles) with external fuel
Weights: normal take-off 16,100kg (35,495lb)
Dimensions: span 12m (39ft 4.5in); length 18.7m (61ft 4.5in); wing area 73m² (785.8sq ft)

A twin-turbofan scale-up of the Mirage 2000: the Super Mirage 4000 resumed flying in 1986, in support of the Rafale programme

Dassault-Breguet Rafale-A

Country of origin: France
Type: multi-role tactical fighter
First flight: July 1986
Accommodation: pilot on reclining seat
Armament (fixed): one 30mm cannon
Armament (disposable): up to unstated weight
Electronics and operational equipment: fly-by-wire control system, wide-angle head-up display, voice command and voice warning systems
Powerplant and fuel system: two General Electric F404-GE-400 afterburning turbofans, rated at 71.2kN (16,000lb) thrust each
Performance: maximum speed 2,125km/h (1,300mph); service ceiling not available; range 600-km (373-mile) radius with a 3,500kg (7,716lb) warload on a hi-lo-hi mission
Weights: empty 9,250kg (20,932lb); loaded 20,000kg (44,092lb)
Dimensions: span 11.0m (36ft 1in); length 15.80m (51ft 10in); height not available; wing area 47.00m² (505.92sq ft)

France's main combat aircraft of the
1990s

Dassault-Breguet/Dornier Alpha Jet

Country of origin: France/West Germany
Type: advanced jet trainer and battlefield close-support/reconnaissance aircraft
First flight: October 1973
Accommodation: pupil and instructor seated in tandem on Martin-Baker AJRM4 (French aircraft)
Armament (fixed): one Mauser 27mm or DEFA 30mm cannon
Armament (disposable): up to a maximum of 2,500kg (5,511lb)
Electronics and operational equipment: communication and navigation equipment
Powerplant and fuel system: two 1,350kg (2,976lb) thrust SNECMA/Turboméca Larzac 04-C5 turbofans
Performance: maximum speed 1,005km/h (624mph) or Mach 0.85 at 3,050m (10,000ft); service ceiling 14,630m (48,000ft); range 425km (264 miles)
Weights: normal take-off 5,000kg (11,023lb) as a trainer; maximum take-off 7,500kg (16,534lb) for attack
Dimensions: span 9.11m (29ft 10.75in); length 12.29m (40ft 3.75in) as a trainer, and 13.23m (43ft 5in) as an attack aircraft; wing area 17.5m² (188.4sq ft)

The highly successful Alpha Jet is in service with 12 air forces

de Havilland D.H.100 Vampire FB Mk 5

Country of origin: UK
Type: strike fighter
First flight: September 1943
Accommodation: pilot
Armament (fixed): four 20mm cannon
Armament (disposable): up to 904kg (2,000lb)
Electronics and operational equipment: communications and navigation equipment
Powerplant and fuel system: one 1,420kgp (3,100lb) de Havilland Goblin 2 turbojet
Performance: maximum speed 861km/h (535mph) at 5,791m (19,000ft); service ceiling 12,192m (40,000ft); range 1,883km (1,170 miles) with maximum fuel
Weights: empty 3,310kg (7,253lb); maximum take-off weight 5,600kg (12,290lb)
Dimensions: span 11.6m (38ft); length 9.37m (30ft 9in); wing area 28.7m² (266 sq ft)

The UK's second turbojet-powered fighter, but too late to see service in World War II

de Havilland (Hawker Siddeley) D.H.110 Sea Vixen FAW.Mk 2

Country of origin: UK
Type: carrierborne all-weather night fighter
First flight: June 1955
Accommodation: two
Armament (fixed): none
Armament (disposable): four short-range air-to-air missiles (Red Top or Firestreak) plus two packs each with fourteen 51mm (2 in) folding fin anti-aircraft rockets
Powerplant: two 5,102kgp (11,250lb) Rolls-Royce Avon Mk.208 turbojets
Performance: maximum speed 1,070km/h (577mph) or Mach 0.94 at 6,096m (20,000ft); service ceiling 14,630m (48,000ft); range 1,271km (686 naut miles) on internal fuel only
Weights: maximum take-off weight 16,783kg (37,000lb)
Dimensions: span 15.24m (50ft); length 16.94m (55.58ft); wing area 62.2m² (648sq ft)

Originally designed for the RAF, before being switched to Naval use

Douglas F4D-1 Skyray

Country of origin: USA
Type: carrierborne interceptor
First flight: January 1951
Accommodation: pilot
Armament (fixed): four 20mm cannon
Armament (disposable): four short-range air-to-air missiles
Electronics and operational equipment: communications and navigation equipment
Powerplant: one 7,258kgp (16,000lb) Pratt & Whitney J57-P-8B turbojet with reheat
Performance: maximum speed 1,154km/h (717mph) at sea level; service ceiling 11,460m (37,500ft); range 1,803km (1,120 miles) at altitude
Weights: empty 7,268kg (16,024lb); maximum take-off weight 12,701kg (28,000lb) – catapult limit
Dimensions: span 10.21m (33ft 6in); length 13.84m (45ft 4in); wing area 51.74m² (557sq ft)

Another of America's early delta-winged aircraft, it suffered problems with development of the Westinghouse XJ40 engines, and finally entered service with Pratt & Whitney J57-P-2 afterburners

Eurofighter EFA

Country of origin: Italy/Spain/UK/West Germany
First flight: August 1986
Enters service: due in 1996
Accommodation: pilot
Armament (fixed): one cannon
Armament (disposable): up to 4,500kg (9,920lb) of air-to-air missiles
Electronics and operational equipment: fly-by-wire control systems and communication systems
Powerplant and fuel system: two Eurojet EJ200 advanced technology afterburning turbofans, rated at 90kN (20,250lb) thrust each
Performance: maximum speed 2,200km/h (1,368mph); service ceiling not available; range 556 km (345 miles) with typical warload
Weights: empty 9,750kg (21,945lb); loaded 17,000kg (37,480lb)
Dimensions: span 10.50m (34ft 5.5in); length 14.50m (47ft 7in); height not available; wing area not available

The EFA resembles the Rafale, but is larger and far more sophisticated

Fairchild Republic A-10A Thunderbolt II

Country of origin: USA
Type: close-support aircraft
First flight: May 1972
Accommodation: pilot seated on a Douglas ACES II ejector seat
Armament (fixed): one General Electric GAU-8/A Avenger rotary-barrel 30mm cannon in the forward fuselage with 1,174 rounds
Armament (disposable): the maximum external load with reduced fuel is 7,258kg (16,000lb), reducing to 5,505kg (14,340lb) with a maximum fuel load
Electronics and operational equipment: communication and navigation equipment
Powerplant and fuel system: two 4,111kg (9,065lb) thrust General Electric TF34-GE-100 turbofans
Performance: maximum speed 706km/h (439mph) at sea-level in clean condition; range 463-km (288-mile) close-air support radius with a 1.7-hour loiter, or 3,950km (2,455 miles) for ferrying against a 93km/h (58mph) wind
Weights: empty 11,322kg (24,960lb); maximum take-off 22,680kg (50,000lb)
Dimensions: span 17.53m (57ft 6in); length 16.26m (53ft 4in); height 4.47m (14ft 8in); wing area 47.01m² (506sq ft)
Aircraft in service: USA 650 +

A-10As take off for air-to-ground gunnery training

Folland Gnat F.Mk 1

Country of origin: UK
Type: fighter
First flight: July 1955
Accommodation: pilot
Armament (fixed): two 30mm cannon
Armament (disposable): up to 454kg (1,000lb) bombs
Powerplant: one 2,132kgp (4,700lb) Bristol Siddeley Orpheus 701 turbojet
Performance: maximum speed 1,118km/h (604kt) or Mach 0.98 at 6,096m (20,000ft); service ceiling 15,240m (50,000ft); range 805km (500 miles) with additional fuel
Weights: empty 2,302kg (5,074lb); maximum take-off weight 4,032kg (8,885lb)
Dimensions: span 6.76m (22.16ft); length 9.07m (29.75ft); wing area 12.69m² (136.6sq ft)

The Gnat T.Mk1 with slightly lengthened two-seater fuselage

General Dynamics F-16A Fighting Falcon

Country of origin: USA
Type: lightweight air-combat fighter
First flight: December 1982
Accommodation: pilot
Armament: one General Electric M61A1 Vulcan rotary-barrel 20mm cannon in the port wing/fuselage fairing with 500 rounds. Disposable load is 9,276kg (20,450lb)
Electronics and operational equipment: communication and navigation equipment, plus Westinghouse AN/APG-66 pulse-Doppler range and angle track radar (with look-down and look-up ranges of 56km [35 miles] and 74km [46 miles] respectively)
Powerplant and fuel system: one 11,340kg (25,000lb) afterburning thrust Pratt & Whitney F100-PW-200 turbofan
Performance: maximum speed more than 2,124km/lh (1,320mph); service ceiling more than 15,240m (50,000ft); range more than 925-km (575-mile) combat radius
Weights: empty 8,065kg (17,780lb); normal take-off 11,633kg (25,674lb)
Dimensions: span 9.45m (31ft) over missile rails; length 15.09m (49ft 5.9in); height 5.09m (16ft 8.5in); wing area 27.87m² (300sq ft)
Production (all variants): 3,081 aircraft

The highly acclaimed and brilliantly capable F-16A of the Belgian Air
74 *Force*

General Dynamics F-111F

Country of origin: USA
Type: variable-geometry multi-role fighter
First flight: December 1964
Accommodation: crew of two side-by-side
Armament (fixed): one General Electric M61A1 Vulcan 20mm cannon (optional)
Armament (disposable): this is carried in an internal weapons bay and on four underwing hardpoints; the former bay can carry two 340kg (750lb) B43 nuclear free-fall bombs; maximum ordnance load is 14,288kg (31,500lb)
Electronics and operational equipment: communication and navigation equipment, plus General Electric AN/APQ-119 attack and navigation radar, Texas Instruments AN/APQ-128 terrain-following radar
Powerplant and fuel system: two 11,385kg (25,100lb) afterburning thrust Pratt & Whitney TF30-PW-100 turbofans; can refuel in flight
Performance: maximum speed 2,655km/h (1,650mph); range more than 4,707km (2,925 miles)
Weights: empty 21,398kg (47,175lb); maximum take-off 45,359kg (100,000lb)
Dimensions: span 19m (63ft) spread and 9.74m (31ft 11.4in) swept; length 22.4m (73ft 6in); height 5.22m (17ft 1.4in); wing area 48.77m² (525sq ft) spread and 61.07m² (657.3sq ft) swept

An F-111F of the 48th TFW releases 227kg (500lb) bombs

Gloster Javelin F(AW).Mk 9

Country of origin: UK
Type: all-weather night fighter
First flight: November 1951
Accommodation: two
Armament (fixed): four 30mm cannon
Armament (disposable): four short-range Firestreak air-to-air missiles
Electronics and operational equipment: communications and navigation equipment plus APQ-43 radar
Powerplant: two 4,900kgp (11,000lb) Armstrong Siddeley Sapphire Sa7R with limited reheat
Performance: maximum speed 989km/h (534kt) or Mach 0.926 at 10,670m (35,000ft); service ceiling 15,849m (52,000ft); endurance 1.75 hours with external fuel
Weights: empty 12,610kg (27,800lb); maximum take-off 19,578kg (43,165lb)
Dimensions: span 15.85m (52ft); length 17.3m (56ft 9in); wing area 86m² (927sq ft)

The RAF's first production delta-winged aircraft, and its first purpose-designed all-weather fighter

Gloster Meteor F.Mk 8

Country of origin: UK
Type: fighter
First flight: March 1943
Entered service: July 1944
Accommodation: pilot
Armament (fixed): four 20mm cannon
Armament (disposable): none
Electronics and operational equipment: communications and navigation equipment
Powerplant: two 1,723kgp (3,800lb) Rolls-Royce Derwent 9 turbojets
Performance: maximum speed 962km/h (598 mph) at 3,048m (10,000ft); service ceiling 13,106m (43,000ft); endurance 1.2 hours with ventral and wing fuel tanks
Weights: empty 4,846kg (10,684lb); maximum take-off 7,121kg (15,700lb)
Dimensions: span 11.33m (37.16ft); length 13.59m (44.58ft); wing area 32.5m² (350sq ft)

Grumman F9F-5 Panther

Country of origin: USA
Type: carrierborne fighter
First flight: November 1948
Accommodation: pilot
Armament (fixed): four 20mm cannon
Armament (disposable): up to 1,361kg (3,000lb) bombs
Electronics and operational equipment: communications and navigation equipment
Powerplant: one 3,175kgp (7,000lb) Pratt & Whitney J48-P-2 turbojet
Performance: maximum speed 972km/h (604mph) at sea level; service ceiling 13,045m (42,800ft); range 2,093km (1,300 miles) at altitude
Weights: empty 4,605kg (10,147lb); maximum take-off weight 9,344kg (20,600lb)
Dimensions: span 11.58m (37.99ft); length 11.84m (38.85ft); wing area 23.22m² (250sq ft)

One of the USA Navy's most important fighters of the Korean War, the F9F-5 was the major variant

Grumman F-14A Tomcat

Country of origin: USA
Type: shipboard variable-geometry multi-role fighter
First flight: December 1970
Accommodation: pilot and systems officer
Armament (fixed): one General Electric M61A1 Vulcan rotary-barrel 20mm cannon
Armament (disposable): this is carried on four underfuselage points and on two hard-points, up to a maximum weight of 6,577kg (14,500lb)
Electronics and operational equipment: communication and navigation equipment, plus Hughes AN/AWG-9 weapon control system
Powerplant and fuel system: two 9,480kg (20,900lb) afterburning thrust Pratt & Whitney TF30-P-412A turbofans
Performance: maximum speed 2,486km/h (1,545mph); range about 3,219km (2,000 miles)
Weights: empty 18,036kg (39,762lb); normal take-off 26,533kg (58,539lb); maximum take-off 33,724kg (74,348lb)
Dimensions: span 19.54m (64ft 1.5in) spread and 11.65m (38ft 2.5in) swept; length 19.10m (62ft 8in); height 4.88m (16ft); wing area 52.49m² (565sq ft) spread
Production: USA 600, Iran 79

Lift-off for an F-14A of VF-33

Hindustan Aeronautics Ltd Ajeet

Country of origin: India
Type: lightweight interceptor and attack aircraft
First flight: July 1955, as the Folland Gnat
Armament (fixed): two Aden Mk 4 30mm cannon with 90 rounds per gun
Armament (disposable): this is carried on four underwing hardpoints, the inner pair each capable of accepting a 227kg (500lb) bomb
Electronics and operational equipment: communication and navigation equipment, plus a Ferranti F 195R/3 ISIS weapon sight
Powerplant and fuel system: one 2,041kg (4,500lb) thrust Rolls-Royce Orpheus Mk 701-01 turbojet, and a total internal fuel capacity of 1,350 litres (279 Imp gal) in nine fuselage and two integral fuel tanks
Performance: maximum speed 1,022km/h (635mph); climb to 11,890m (39,000ft) in 6 minutes 2 seconds from brakes-off; service ceiling 13,715m (45,000ft); range 172-km (107-mile) radius
Weights: empty 2,307kg (5,085lb); normal take-off 3,538kg (7,800lb); maximum take-off 4,173kg (9,200lb)
Dimensions: span 6.73m (22ft 1in); length 9.04m (29ft 8in); height 2.46m (8ft 1in); wing area 12.69m² (136.6sq ft)

Produced under licence by HAL, this lightweight fighter was pioneered by Folland as the Fo141 Gnat

Israel Aircraft Industries Kfir-C2

Country of origin: Israel
Type: interceptor and ground-attack aircraft
First flight: 1973
Accommodation: pilot
Armament (fixed): two DEFA 552 30mm cannon with 140 rounds per gun
Armament (disposable): up to a maximum weight of 5,775kg (12,731lb)
Electronics and operational equipment: communication and navigation equipment
Powerplant and fuel system: one 8,119kg (17,900lb) afterburning thrust General Electric J79-J1E turbojet
Performance: maximum speed over 2,440km/h (1,516mph) or Mach 2.3 at 11,000m (36,090ft), and 1,390km/h (864mph) or Mach 1.1 at sea level; service ceiling 17,680m (58,000ft) in stable flight in air-combat configuration; range 345km (214 miles)
Weights: empty 7,285kg (16,060lb); normal take-off 9,390kg (20,701lb) for interception or 14,670kg (32,341lb) for ground-attack; maximum take-off 16,200kg (35,714lb)
Dimensions: span 8.22m (26ft 11.5in) for wing, and 3.73m (12ft 3in) for canard; length 15.65m (51ft 4.5in) including probe; wing area 34.8m² (374.6sq ft)
Production: 225 aircraft

Israeli Air Force Kfir-C2s, based on the Mirage 5

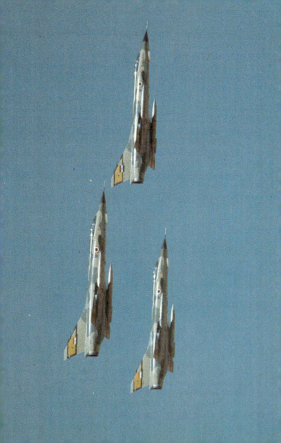

Lockheed F-80B Shooting Star

Country of origin: USA
Type: fighter
First flight: January 1944
Entered service: January 1945
Accommodation: pilot
Armament (fixed): six 18.5mm (.5in) machine guns
Armament (disposable): none
Electronics and operational equipment: communication and navigation equipment
Powerplant and fuel system: one 2,041kgp (4,500lb) Allison J33-A-21 turbojet
Performance: maximum speed 929km/h (577mph) at 1,830m (6,000ft); service ceiling 13,870m (45,500ft); range 1,270km (790 miles) without drop-tanks
Weights: empty 3,709kg (8,176lb); maximum take-off 7,257kg (16,000lb)
Dimensions: span 11.81m (38.75ft); length 10.49m (34.42ft); wing area 22.07m² (237.6sq ft)
Production: 5,691 all variants

Just too late to see service in World War II, but undoubtedly the best jet fighter to emerge from that era

Lockheed F-104G Starfighter

Country of origin: USA
Type: multi-role fighter
First flight: February 1954
Accommodation: pilot seated on a Martin-Baker Mk GQ7(F) ejector seat
Armament (fixed): one General Electric M61A-1 Vulcan rotary-barrel 30mm cannon with 750 rounds in the nose
Armament (disposable): up to a maximum weight of 1,955kg (4,310lb)
Electronics and operational equipment: communication and navigation equipment, fire-control radar system, General Electric AN/ASG-14 optical sight system, automatic flight-control system and an inertial navigation system
Powerplant and fuel system: one 7,167kg (15,800lb) afterburning thrust General Electric J79-GE-11A or MAN/Turbo-Union J79-MTU-J1K
Performance: maximum speed 2,333km/h (1,450mph) at 10,970m (36,000ft); service ceiling 17,680m (58,000ft); range 2,495km (1,550 miles)
Weights: 6,758kg (14,900lb); normal take-off 9,838kg (21,690lb)
Dimensions: span 6.68m (21ft 11in); length 16.69m (54ft 9in); wing area 18.22m² (196.1sq ft)

Production totalled 1,286 until cessation in 1983

Lockheed F-117A

Country of origin: USA
Type: 'stealth' penetration strike fighter
First flight: 1981, revealed 1988
Accommodation: pilot on an ejector seat
Armament (fixed): none
Armament (disposable): this is carried in a paired lower-fuselage weapons bay, up to a maximum weight of about 1,814kg (4,000lb) of specialised anti-radiation and comparable 'smart' weapons
Electronics and operational equipment: communications and navigation equipment
Powerplant and fuel system: probably two 5,443kg (12,000lb) thrust General Electric F404 non-afterburning turbofans, and an internal fuel capacity of unrevealed quantity
Performance: highly classified, but probably including subsonic speed at altitude and a combat radius of about 805km (500 miles)
Weights: empty about 6,804kg (15,000lb); maximum take-off about 13,608kg (30,000lb)
Dimensions: span about 12.8m (42ft); length about 20.5m (67ft 3in); height about 3.66m (12ft); wing area not revealed
Production: 59 aircraft

First of the USA's 'stealth' fighters, designed to trap enemy radar emissions and so produce no echo

McDonnell FH-1 Phantom

Country of origin: USA
Type: carrierborne fighter
First flight: January 1945
Accommodation: pilot
Armament (fixed): four 18.5mm (.5in) machine guns
Armament (disposable): none
Electronics and operational equipment: communications and navigation equipment
Powerplant: two 726kgp (1,600lb) Westinghouse J30-WE-20 turbojets
Performance: maximum speed 784km/h (487mph) at sea level; service ceiling 13.320m (43,700ft); range 870km (540 miles) on internal fuel only
Weights: empty 2,792kg (6,156lb); maximum take-off 4,323kg (9,531lb)
Dimensions: span 12.42m (40ft 9in); length 11.35m (37ft 3in); wing area 25.6m² (276sq ft)
Production: 100 aircraft

McDonnell F3H-2N/F-3C Demon

Country of origin: USA
Type: carrierborne fighter
First flight: August 1951
Entered service: December 1953
Accommodation: pilot
Armament (fixed): four 20mm cannon
Armament (disposable): four short-range Sidewinder IR-homing air-to-air missiles
Electronics and operational equipment: communication and navigation equipment
Powerplant: one 6,350kgp (14,000lb) Allison J71-A-2 turbojet with reheat
Performance: maximum speed 1,170km/h (727mph) at sea level; service ceiling 13,000m (42,650ft); range 1,900km (1,180 miles) with combat load
Weights: empty 9,656kg (21,287lb); maximum take-off 15,161kg (33,424lb)
Dimensions: span 10.77m (35.33ft); length 17.98m (59ft); wing area 48.2m² (519sq ft)
Production: 140 aircraft

The F3H-2N was a larger variant of the initial F3H-1N, which entered service in December 1953

McDonnell Douglas CF-101B Voodoo

Country of origin: USA
Type: long-range interceptor fighter
First flight: September 1954
Accommodation: pilot and weapons officer
Armament (fixed): none
Armament (disposable): comprises three Hughes AIM-4D Falcon air-to-air missiles in the weapons bay and two Douglas Air-2A Genie
Electronics and operational equipment: communication and navigation equipment, plus MG-13 fire-control system with automatic search and tracking
Powerplant and fuel system: two 7,666kg (16,900lb) afterburning thrust Pratt & Whitney J57-P-55 turbojets, and a total internal fuel capacity of 7,771 litres (1,709 Imp gal)
Performance: maximum speed 1,835km/h (1,134mph) at 10,670m (35,000ft); service ceiling 16,705m (54,800ft); range 2,445km (1,520 miles)
Weights: empty 13,141kg (28,970lb); normal take-off 20,713kg (45,664lb); maximum take-off 23,768kg (52,400lb)
Dimensions: span 12.09m (39ft 8in); length 20.55m (67ft 5in); height 5.49m (18ft); wing area 34.19m² (368sq ft)

The CF-101s were operated by the Royal Canadian Air Force: the initial model F-101A entered service as a tactical fighter

McDonnell Douglas F/A-18A Hornet

Country of origin: USA
Type: shipboard strike fighter
First flight: November 1979
Accommodation: pilot
Armament: one General Electric M61A1 Vulcan rotary-barrel 20mm cannon in the nose; maximum load is 7,711kg (17,000lb)
Electronics and operational equipment: communication and navigation equipment, plus multi-mode air-to-air and air-to-surface tracking radar, head-up display, radar-warning receiver, inertial navigation system and flight-control system with two digital computers
Powerplant and fuel system: two 7,257kg (16,000lb) afterburning thrust General Electric F404-GE-400 turbofans
Performance: maximum speed more than 1,915km/h (1,190mph); service ceiling 15,240m (50,000ft); range more than 740-km (460-mile) radius
Weights: empty 9,331kg (20,570lb); normal take-off 15,234kg (33,585lb) for a fighter mission; maximum take-off 21,887kg (48,252lb) for an attack mission
Dimensions: span 11.43m (36ft 6in) without missiles; length 17.07m (56ft); height 4.66m (15ft 3.5in); wing area 37.16m² (400sq ft)
Production (all variants): 1,477 aircraft

F/A-18 prepares for launch aboard

USS Constellation

McDonnell Douglas F-4E Phantom II

Country of origin: USA
Type: all-weather multi-role fighter
Entered service: 1964
Accommodation: two seated in tandem
Armament (fixed): one 20mm General Electric M61A1 Vulcan rotary-barrel cannon with 640 rounds
Armament (disposable): this is accommodated on four recessed stations under the fuselage and five hardpoints
Electronics and operational equipment: communication and navigation equipment plus all-altitude bombing system, weapons release system and CPK-92A computer
Powerplant and fuel system: two 8,119kg (17,900lb) thrust General Electric J79-GE-17A afterburning turbojets
Performance: maximum speed (clean) 2,301km/h (1,430mph); initial climb rate (clean) 15,180m (49,800ft) per minute; service ceiling (clean) 17,905m (58,750ft); range 1,145-km (712-mile) combat radius
Weights: empty 13,757kg (30,328lb); normal take-off 18,818kg (41,487lb); maximum take-off 28,030kg (61,795lb)
Dimensions: span 11.77m (38ft 7.5in); length 19.20m (63ft); height 5.02m (16ft 5.5in); wing area 49.24m² (530sq ft)

An F-4E in USAF markings before
delivery to the Israeli Air Force

McDonnell Douglas F-15C Eagle

Country of origin: USA
Type: air-superiority and attack fighter
First flight: June 1985
Accommodation: pilot
Armament (fixed): one General Electric M61A1 Vulcan 20mm cannon with 940 rounds
Armament (disposable): carried on special positions and on three underfuselage and two underwing hardpoints, up to a maximum of 7,257kg (16,000lb)
Electronics and operational equipment: communication and navigation equipment, plus search and tracking radar and head-up display
Powerplant and fuel system: two 10,864kg (23,950lb) afterburning thrust Pratt & Whitney F100-PW-100 turbofans
Performance: maximum speed more than 2,655km/h (1,650mph); absolute ceiling 30,480m (100,000ft); range more than 4,631km (2,878 miles) without FAST packs but with drop-tanks
Weights: empty 12,700kg (28,000lb); normal take-off 20,212kg (44,560lb); maximum take-off 30,845kg (68,000lb)
Dimensions: span 13.05m (42ft 9.75in); length 19.43m (63ft 9in); height 5.63m (18ft 5.5in); wing area 56.5m² (608sq ft)
Production (all variants): 1,569 aircraft

A pair of F-15 Eagles lifts off from
Bitburg AB in Germany

McDonnell Douglas/British Aerospace AV-8B Harrier II

Country of origin: USA/UK
Type: V/STOL close-support aircraft
First flight: November 1978
Accommodation: pilot seated on a Stencel ejector seat (US aircraft)
Armament (fixed): one General Electric GAU-12/A 25mm rotary-barrel cannon system
Armament (disposable): to a maximum of 3,175kg (7,000lb)
Electronics and operational equipment: communication and navigation equipment, plus a Garrett digital air-data computer, inertial navigation system, 360° radar-warning receiver
Powerplant and fuel system: one 9,979kg (22,000lb) vectored-thrust Rolls-Royce Pegasus 11-21 (F402-RR-406) turbofan
Performance: maximum speed 988km/h (615mph) or Mach 0.93 at 10,970m (36,000ft); range 282-km (172-mile) radius with 12 Mk 82 Snakeye bombs
Weights: empty 5,783kg (12,750lb); normal take-off 10,410kg (22,950lb); maximum take-off 13,494kg (29,750lb)
Dimensions: span 9.25m (30ft 4in); length 14.12m (46ft 4in); height 3.55m (11ft 7.75in); wing area 21.37m² (230sq ft)
Production: 436 aircraft

The large carbon-fibre wing of the AV-8B features outriggers located at mid-span

McDonnell Douglas/Israel Aircraft Industries Phantom 2000

Country of origin: Israel
Type: multi-role interceptor and ground attack fighter
Entered service: 1989
Accommodation: two
Armament (fixed): one 20mm M61A1 Vulcan six-barrel cannon
Armament (disposable): up to 7,257kg (16,000lb)
Electronics and operational equipment: communications and navigation equipment plus HOTAS (Hands On Throttle And Stick) controls, head-down displays and a wide-angle head-up display
Powerplant and fuel system: two General Electric J79-GE-17 afterburning turbojets each rated at 79.65kN (17,900lb) thrust
Performance: maximum speed 2,301km/h (1,430mph); service ceiling 17,905m (58,750ft); range 1,145km (712 miles) radius on a hi-lo-hi mission
Weights: not availaable
Dimensions: span 11.77m (38ft 7.5in); length 19.20m (63ft); height 5.02m (16ft 5.5in); wing area 49.24m² (530sq ft)

Based on the F-4E Phantom II, the type has been continually upgraded since entering service

Mikoyan-Gurevich MiG-15*bis* 'Fagot'

Country of origin: USSR
Type: fighter
First flight: 1947
Accommodation: pilot seated on an ejector seat
Armament: one N-37 37mm cannon with 40 rounds and two NR-23 23mm cannon with 80 rounds per gun in the nose; maximum weight of 1,000kg (2,205lb) of bombs or rockets
Electronics and operational equipment: communication and navigation equipment
Powerplant and fuel system: one 3,170kg (6,989lb) thrust Klimov VK-1A turbojet
Performance: maximum speed 1,100km/h (684mph) at 12,000m (39,370ft); service ceiling 15,550m (51,015ft); range 2,000km (1,232 miles) with maximum fuel
Weights: empty 3,400kg (7,495lb); normal take-off 4,960kg (10,934lb)
Dimensions: span 10.08m (33ft 0.75in); length 11.05m (36ft 3.5in); height 3.4m (11ft 1.75in); wing area 20.6m² (221.7sq ft)
Production: this ran to many thousand aircraft in addition to being licensed for production in both Czechoslovakia and Poland

*The MiG-15 was the USSR's first mass-production swept-wing fighter, and the MiG-15*bis *its major variant*

Mikoyan-Gurevich MiG-17F 'Fresco-C'

Country of origin: USSR
Type: fighter
Entered service: 1952
Accommodation: pilot seated on an ejector seat
Armament (fixed): one N-37D 37mm cannon with 40 rounds and two NR-23 23mm cannon with 80 rounds
Armament (disposable): up to 500kg (1,102lb) of bombs or unguided rockets
Electronics and operational equipment: communication and navigation equipment
Powerplant and fuel system: one 3,400kg (7,495lb) afterburning thrust Klimov VK-1F turbojet with reheat
Performance: maximum speed 1,145km/h (711mph) at 4,000m (13,132ft) or Mach 0.97 at 3,000m (9,840ft); initial climb rate 3,900m (12,795ft) per minute; service ceiling 16,600m (54,460ft); range 1,470km (913 miles)
Weights: empty 4,100kg (9,040lb); normal take-off 5,340kg (11,773lb); maximum take-off 6,700kg (14,770lb)
Dimensions: span 9.63m (31ft 7in); length 11.26m (36ft 11.25in); height 3.35m (11ft); wing area 22.6m² (243.3sq ft)

Mikoykan-Gurevich MiG-19SF 'Farmer-C'

Country of origin: USSR
Type: fighter
First flight: September 1953
Accommodation: pilot on an ejector seat
Armament (fixed): three NR-30 30mm cannon
Armament (disposable): this is carried on two underwing hardpoints, and can consist of two AA-2 'Atoll' air-to-air missiles, or two 212mm (8.35in) rockets, or two packs each with eight 57mm (2.24in) rockets, or two 250 or 500kg (551 or 1,102lb) bombs
Electronics and operational equipment: communication and navigation equipment
Powerplant and fuel system: two 3,250kg (7,165lb) afterburning thrust Klimov RD-9BF turbojets
Performance: maximum speed 1,450km/h (901mph) at 10,000m (32,810ft); service ceiling 17,900m (58,725ft); range 1,390km (863 miles)
Weights: empty 5,170kg (11,397lb); normal take-off 7,400kg (16,314lb);maximum take-off 8,900kg (19,621lb)
Dimensions: span 9.2m (30ft 2.25in); length 12.6m (41ft 4in) excluding probe; height 3.9m (12ft 9.5in); wing area 25m² (269.1sq ft)

The MiG-19 and the Super Sabre vied to become the first genuinely supersonic fighter

Mikoyan-Gurevich MiG-21MF 'Fishbed-J'

Country of origin: USSR
Type: multi-role fighter
First flight: 1957
Accommodation: pilot seated on ejector seat
Armament (fixed): one twin-barrel GSh-23 23mm cannon with 200 rounds in a belly pack
Armament (disposable): this is carried on four underwing hardpoints, up to a maximum weight of about 1,500kg (3,307lb)
Electronics and operational equipment: communication and navigation equipment, plus 'Jay Bird' search and tracking radar in inlet centrebody and a gyro gunsight
Powerplant and fuel system: one 6,600kg (14,550lb) Tumanskii R-13-300 turbojet
Performance: maximum speed 2,230km/h (1,385mph) or Mach 2.1 at 11,000m (36,090ft) and 1,300km/h (807mph) or Mach 1.06 at sea level; service ceiling about 15,250m (50,030ft); range 370km (230 miles)
Weights: normal take-off 8,200kg (18,077lb) with four AA-2 missiles; maximum take-off 9,400kg (20,723lb) with missiles and drop-tanks
Dimensions: span 7.15m (23ft 5.5in); length 15.76m (51ft 8.5in) including probe; height 4.10m (13ft 5.5in); wing area 23m² (247.6sq ft)

In its day, one of the world's most important fighters

Mikoyan-Gurevich MiG-23MF 'Flogger-G'

Country of origin: USSR
Type: variable-geometry air-combat fighter
First flight: 1966
Accommodation: pilot
Armament: one GSh-23 23mm twin-barrel cannon in a fuselage belly pack; maximum of about 2,000kg (4,409lb) of stores
Electronics and operational equipment: communication and navigation equipment, plus 'High Lark' search radar
Powerplant and fuel system: one 12,475kg (27,502lb) afterburning thrust Tumanskii R-29 turbojet, and a total internal capacity of 5,750 litres (1,265 Imp gal), plus provision for one 800-litre (176-Imp gal) drop tank on the centre-line hardpoint
Performance: maximum speed 2,500km/h (1,553mph), at high altitude; service ceiling 18,600m (61,025ft); combat radius between 900 and 1,200km (560 and 745 miles)
Weights: normal take-off 12,700kg (27,998lb); maximum take-off 16,000kg (35,273lb)
Dimensions: span spread 14.25m (46ft 9in) and swept 8.17m (26ft 9.5in); length 16.8m (55ft 1.5in); height 4.35m (14ft 4in); wing area 37m² (398.3sq ft)
Production: 3,646 aircraft

The mainstay fighter of the Warsaw Pact

Mikoyan-Gurevich MiG-25 'Foxbat-A'

Country of origin: USSR
Type: interceptor fighter
First flight: 1965
Accommodation: pilot only, seated on a KM-1 ejector seat
Armament (fixed): none
Armament (disposable): this is carried on four underwing hardpoints, and generally comprises four AA-6 'Acrid' air-to-air missiles, or two AA-7 'Apex' and two AA-8 'Aphid' air-to-air missiles
Electronics and operational equipment: communication and navigation equipment
Powerplant and fuel system: two 11,000kg (24,250lb) afterburning thrust Tumanskii R-31 turbojets, and a total internal fuel capacity of about 17,400 litres (3,830 Imp gal) in fuselage, inlet saddle and integral wing tanks
Performance: maximum speed 2,975km/h (1,849mph); initial climb rate 12,480m (40,945ft) per minute; service ceiling 24,400m (80,050ft); combat radius 1,130km (702 miles)
Weights: empty about 20,000kg (44,092lb); maximum take-off 36,200kg (79,806lb)
Dimensions: span 13.95m (45ft 9 in); length 23.82m (78ft 1.75in); height 6.1m (20ft 0.25in); wing area 56.83m² (611.7sq ft)
Production: 761 aircraft

Designed to carry AA-6 'Acrids', the world's largest air-to-air missiles

Mikoyan-Gurevich MiG-27 'Flogger-D'

Country of origin: USSR
Type: ground-attack aircraft
Operational: 1978
Accommodation: pilot only
Armament: one 23mm six-barrel rotary cannon in a ventral package plus maximum of 3,000kg (6,614lb) of stores
Electronics and operational equipment: communication and navigation equipment, plus a laser ranger and marked-target seeker and Sirena 3 radar-warning receiver
Powerplant and fuel system: one 11,500kg (25,353lb) afterburning thrust Tumanskii R-29B
Performance: maximum speed 1,595km/h (991mph) or Mach 1.5 at high altitude; service ceiling 16,000m (52,495ft); ferry range with three drop-tanks 2,500km (1,553 miles)
Weights: normal take-off 15,500kg (34,170lb); maximum take-off 18,000kg (39,863lb)
Dimensions: span spread 14.25m (46ft 9in) and swept 8.17m (26ft 9.5in); length 16m (52ft 6in); height 4.35m (14ft 4in); wing area spread 27.26m² (293.4sq ft)
Production: USSR 830, India 165

The 'Flogger-J' variant, introduced
124 *in 1983*

Mikoyan-Gurevich MiG-29 'Fulcrum-A'

Country of origin: USSR
Type: air-superiority and ground attack fighter
Entered service: 1985
Accommodation: pilot
Armament (fixed): one 23mm GSh-23L twin-barrel cannon
Armament (disposable): maximum weight not stated but inclusive of two medium-range and four short-range air-to-air missiles
Electronics and operational equipment: communications and navigation equipment
Powerplant and fuel system: two 8,300kgp (18,300lb) Tumanskii R-33D turbofans with reheat
Performance: maximum speed 2,445km/h (1,519mph); service ceiling 17,000m (55,775ft); range 1,150-km (715-mile) radius on a hi-hi-hi mission
Weights: empty 7,825kg (17,251lb); loaded 18,000kg (39,683lb)
Dimensions: span 11.36m (37ft 3.25in); length 17.32m (56ft 9.85in); height 4.73m (15ft 6.2in); wing area 35.50m² (382.13sq ft)
Production: 762 aircraft

The latest of the Soviet fighters, with highly advanced weapons systems

Mikoyan-Gurevich MiG-31 'Foxhound'

Country of origin: USSR
Type: all-weather interceptor
First flight: 1964
Accommodation: pilot and systems operator in tandem
Armament (fixed): none
Armament (disposable): comprises eight air-to-air missiles, usually AA-9 'Amos' and AA-8 'Aphid' weapons
Electronics and operational equipment: communications and navigation equipment plus pulse-Doppler fire-control radar
Powerplant and fuel system: two 14,000kg (30,864lb) afterburning thrust Tumanskii R-31F turbojets and a total internal fuel capacity of 17,410 litres (3,830 Imp gal)
Performance: maximum speed 2,553km/h (1,586mph) or Mach 2.4 at high altitude; initial climb rate and service ceiling not revealed; radius 1,500km (932 miles)
Weights: empty 21,825kg (48,115lb); maximum take-off 41,150kg (90,725lb)
Dimensions: span 14m (45ft 11.2in); length 25m (82ft 0.25in); height 6.10m (20ft 0.2in); wing area 58m² (624.33sq ft)
Production: 160 aircraft

The 'Foxhound' is based on the earlier MiG-25 'Foxbat'

Mitsubishi F-1

Country of origin: Japan
Type: close-support fighter
First flight: June 1975
Accommodation: pilot seated on a Daiseru-built Weber ES-7J ejector seat
Armament (fixed): one JM61A-1 Vulcan rotary-barrel 20mm cannon
Armament (disposable): this is carried on one underfuselage and four underwing hardpoints, up to a maximum weight of 2,722kg (6,000lb)
Electronics and operational equipment: communication and navigation equipment
Powerplant and fuel system: two 3,207kg (7,070lb) afterburning thrust Rolls-Royce/Turboméca Adour Mk 801A turbofans
Performance: maximum speed 1,700km/h (1,056mph) at 10,790m (36,000ft); range 555-km (345-mile) hi-lo-hi radius with two ASM-1s and one drop-tank
Weights: empty 6,358kg (14,017lb); normal take-off 9,860kg (21,737lb); maximum take-off 13,675kg (30,148lb)
Dimensions: span 7.88m (25ft 10.25in); length 17.84m (58ft 6.25in) including probe; height 4.28m (14ft 4.25in); wing area 21.18m² (288sq ft)

Using the same basic powerplant, the F-1 is a SEPECAT Jaguar lookalike

Nanchang Aircraft Manufacturing Company Q-51 'Fantan A'

Country of origin: China
Type: fighter-bomber
First flight: June 1965
Accommodation: pilot on an ejector seat
Armament (fixed): two 23mm Type 23-2 cannon with 100 rounds per gun
Armament (disposable): carried on ten hard-points up to a maximum of 2,000kg (4,409lb)
Electronics and operational equipment: communications and navigation equipment plus an optical sight and 'High Fix' ranging radar
Powerplant and fuel system: two 3,250kg (7,165lb) afterburning thrust Shenyang Wopen-6 turbojets and a total internal fuel capacity of 3,720 litres (818.5 Imp gal)
Performance: maximum speed 1,190km/h (739mph) or Mach 1.12 at 11,000m (36,090ft); initial climb rate 6,000m (19,685ft) per minute; service ceiling 15,850m (52,000ft); radius 400km (248 miles) on a lo-lo-lo mission with maximum load
Weights: empty 6,495kg (14,319lb; maximum take-off 12,000kg (26,455lb)
Dimensions: span 9.70m (31ft 10in); length 16.255m (53ft 4in); height 4.516m (13ft 9.75in); wing area 29.75m² (300.85sq ft)
Production: 900 aircraft

Built by the Chinese State Factory, these were destined for Pakistan

North American F-86F Sabre

Country of origin: USA
Type: fighter and fighter-bomber
First flight: November 1946
Accommodation: pilot on an ejector seat
Armament (fixed): six 12.7mm (.5in) Colt-Browning M3 machine guns in the nose with 267 rounds per gun
Armament (disposable): provision under the wings for two AIM-9 Sidewinder air-to-air missiles, or two 454kg (1,000lb) bombs, or eight rockets
Electronics and operational equipment: communication and navigation equipment, plus ranging radar in the nose
Powerplant and fuel system: one 2,708kg (5,970lb) thrust General Electric J47-GE-27 turbojet
Performance: maximum speed 1,105km/h (687mph) at sea level; range 1,485km (925 miles) on internal fuel
Weights: empty 5,045kg (11,125lb); normal take-off 7,711kg (17,000lb); maximum take-off 9,350kg (20,610lb)
Dimensions: span 11.91m (39ft 1in); length 11.44m (37ft 6.5in); height 4.47m (14ft 8.75in); wing area 26.76m² (288sq ft)
Production: all countries 9,502

The most important air combat fighter fielded by the Americans in the Korean War

North American F-100D Super Sabre

Country of origin: USA
Type: interceptor and fighter-bomber
First flight: May 1953
Accommodation: pilot seated on an ejector seat
Armament (fixed): four M39 20mm cannon with 200 rounds per gun in the fuselage
Armament (disposable): up to a maximum weight of 3,402kg (7,500lb)
Electronics and operational equipment: communication and navigation equipment, plus attack radar
Powerplant and fuel system: one 7,711kg (17,000lb) afterburning thrust Pratt & Whitney J57-P-21A turbojet
Performance: maximum speed 1,392km/h (865mph) or Mach 1.31 at 10,670m (35,000ft); cruising speed 909km/h (565mph) at 10,970m (36,000ft); initial climb rate 4,875m (16,000ft) per minute; service ceiling 13,715m (45,000ft); range 853-km (530-mile) radius
Weights: empty 9,525kg (21,000lb); maximum take-off 15,800kg (34,830lb)
Dimensions: span 11.81m (38ft 9in); length 16.54m (54ft 3in) including probe; height 4.96m (16ft 2.75in); wing area 35.77m² (385sq ft)

The F-100A entered service in September 1954, and 1,274 units of *the F-100D were later produced*

North American FJ-1 Fury

Country of origin: USA
Type: carrierborne fighter
First flight: January 1945
Accommodation: pilot
Armament (fixed): six 12.5mm (.5in) machine guns
Armament (disposable): none
Electronics and operational equipment: communications and navigation equipment
Powerplant: one 1,814kgp (4,000lb) Allison J35-A-2 turbojet
Performance: maximum speed 880km/h (347mph) at 2,743m (9,000ft); service ceiling 9,754m (32,000ft); range 2,414km (1,500 miles)
Weights: empty 4,011kg (8,843lb); maximum take-off 7,076kg (15,600lb)
Dimensions: span 11.63m (38.16ft); length 10.49m (34.42ft); wing area 20.53m² (221sq ft)
Production: 30 aircraft

The prototype NA-64 was flown with a General Electric J35-GE-2 engine, but the 30 production FJ-1s all had the Allison-developed equivalent

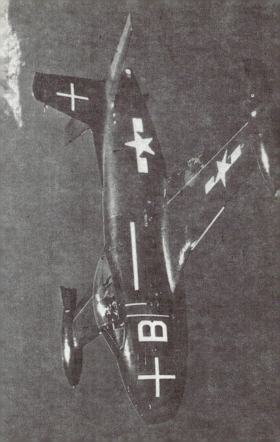

Northrop F-5A Freedom Fighter

Country of origin: USA
Type: lightweight tactical fighter
Entered service: 1972
Accommodation: pilot
Armament (fixed): two Colt-Browning M39 20mm cannon in the nose with 280 rounds per gun
Armament (disposable): this is carried on one underfuselage and four underwing hardpoints and on two wingtip missile-launcher rails, up to 1,996kg (4,400lb)
Electronics and operational equipment: communication and navigation equipment, plus a Norsight optical sight and control equipment for the AGM-12 Bullpup missile when appropriate
Powerplant and fuel system: two 1,850kg (4,080lb) afterburning thrust General Electric J85-GE-13
Performance: maximum speed 1,489km/h (925mph); service ceiling 15,390m (50,500ft); range 314-km (195-mile) radius
Weights: empty 3,667kg (8,085lb); maximum take-off 9,379kg (20,677lb)
Dimensions: span 7.7m (25ft 3in); length 14.38m (47ft 2in); height 4.01m (13ft 2in); wing area 15.79m² (170sq ft)

A total of 818 F-5A Freedom Fighters was built, together with 290 F-5B two-seat variants

Northrop F-5E Tiger II

Country of origin: USA
Type: lightweight tactical fighter
First flight: March 1969
Accommodation: pilot
Armament (fixed): two Colt-Browning M39A2 20mm cannon with 280 rounds per gun in the nose
Armament (disposable): this is carried on one underfuselage and four underwing hardpoints and on two wingtip missile rails, up to a maximum of 3,175kg (7,000lb)
Electronics and operational equipment: communication and navigation equipment, plus AN/APQ-159 lightweight air-to-air search and tracking radar, and AN/ASG-29 optical gunsight
Powerplant and fuel system: two 2,267kg (5,000lb) afterburning thrust General Electric J85-GE-21
Performance: maximum speed 1,730km/h (1,075mph) at 10,970m (36,000ft); initial climb rate 9,630m (31,600ft) per minute; range 305-km (190-mile) radius
Weights: empty 4,275kg (9,425lb); maximum take-off 11,561kg (25,488lb)
Dimensions: span 8.13m (26ft 8in); length 14.73m (48ft 3.75in); height 4.08m (13ft 4.5in); wing area 17.3m² (186sq ft)

F-5Es mimic Soviet appearance and
practice

Northrop F-20 Tigershark

Country of origin: USA
Type: lightweight tactical fighter
First flight: 1982
Accommodation: pilot
Armament (fixed): two Colt-Browning M39A2 20mm cannon with 450 rounds per gun
Armament (disposable): this is carried on one underfuselage and four underwing hardpoints, and on two wingtip missile rails, to a maximum of more than 3,629kg (8,000lb)
Electronics and operational equipment: communication and navigation equipment, plus General Electric GE-200 multi-mode radar
Powerplant and fuel system: one 7,711kg (17,000lb) afterburning thrust General Electric F404-GE-100 turbofan
Performance: maximum speed about 2,125km/h (1,320mph); range 556km (345 miles)
Weights: empty 5,089kg (11,220lb); normal take-off 6,831kg (15,060lb) with half fuel; maximum take-off 11,265kg (26,290lb)
Dimensions: span 8.13m (26ft 8in); length 14.17m (46ft 6in) excluding probe; height 4.22m (13ft 10.25in)

The Tigershark had genuine Mach 2+ performance and extremely good radar, but the project was cancelled late in 1986, owing to lack of orders

Northrop F-89D Scorpion

Country of origin: USA
Type: night/all-weather fighter
First flight: August 1958
Accommodation: two
Armament (fixed): none
Armament (disposable): one hundred and four 70mm (2.75 in) Mighty Mouse rockets
Electronics and operational equipment: communications and navigation equipment
Powerplant: two 3,266kpg (7,200lb) Allison J35-A-35 turbojets with reheat
Performance: maximum speed 1,022km/h (635mph) at 3,231m (10,600ft); service ceiling 15,000m (49,217ft); range 2,205km (1,370 miles)
Weights: empty 11,428kg (25,194lb); maximum take-off 21,219kg (46,780lb)
Dimensions: span 18.41m (60.42ft); length 16.41m (53.83ft); wing area 52.21m² (562sq ft)
Production: 682 aircraft

The 89A, 89B and 89C all had six 20mm cannon, which were replaced in the F-89D by the unguided air-to-air rockets

Panavia Tornado ADV

Country of origin: UK/West Germany/Italy
Type: variable-geometry STOL all-weather air-defence interceptor fighter
First flight: August 1974
Accommodation: pilot and systems operator in tandem
Armament: (fixed): one 27mm Mauser BK27 cannon with 180 rounds per gun
Armament (disposable): carried on four semi-recessed missile stations under the fuselage and two underwing hardpoints
Electronics and operational equipment: communications and navigation equipment plus GEC Avionics A1-24 Foxhunter pulse-Doppler
Powerplant and fuel system: two 7,675kg (16,290lb) afterburning thrust Turbo-Union RB.199-34R Mk 103 turbofans and a total internal fuel capacity of 7,250 litres (1,595 Imp gal)
Performance: maximum speed 2,337km/h (1,453 mph); service ceiling about 21,335m (70,000ft); radius 1,850km (1,150 miles)
Weights: empty 14,500kg (31,996lb); maximum take-off 27,986kg (61,700lb)
Dimensions: span 13.91m (45ft 7.5in) spread, and 8.6m (28ft 2.5in) swept; length 18.082m (59ft 4in); height 5.95m (28ft 2.5in); wing area about 25m² (269.1sq ft)
Production: 197 aircraft

Saudi Air Force ADV, armed with Sky Flash and Sidewinders

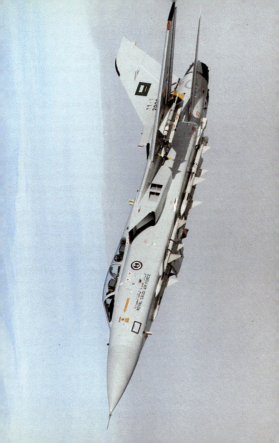

Panavia Tornado IDS

Country of origin: Italy/UK/West Germany
Type: variable-geometry multi-role combat aircraft
First flight: August 1974
Accommodation: pilot and systems operator seated in tandem on ejector seats
Armament (fixed): two IWKA-Mauser 27mm cannon with 360 rounds per gun
Armament (disposable): up to a weight of about 8,165kg (18,000lb)
Electronics and operational equipment: communication and navigation equipment, plus multi-mode forward-looking radar
Powerplant and fuel system: two 7,620kg (16,800lb) afterburning thrust Turbo-Union RB.199-34R Mk 103 turbofans
Performance: maximum speed more than 2,125km/h (1,320mph); service ceiling more than 15,000m (49,210ft); range 1,390m (863 miles)
Weights: normal take-off 20,410kg (44,996lb) with maximum internal fuel but no stores; maximum take-off 26,490kg (58,399lb)
Dimensions: span 13.9m (45ft 7.25in) spread, and 8.60m (28ft 2.5in) swept; length 16.7m (54ft 9.5in); height 5.7m (18ft 8.5in); wing area about 25m² (269sq ft)
Production: 710 aircraft

Tornado IDS of the German Air Force left and German Navy

Republic F-84B Thunderjet

Country of origin: USA
Type: fighter bomber
First flight: February 1946
Accommodation: pilot
Armament (fixed): six 12.5mm (.5in) machine guns
Armament (disposable): thirty-two 127mm (5in) rocket projectiles
Powerplant: one 1,814kgp (4,000lb) Allison J35-A-15 turbojet
Performance: maximum speed 945km/h (587mph) at 1,219m (4,000ft); service ceiling 12,421m (40,750ft); range 2,063km (1,282 miles)
Weights: empty 4,326kg (9,538lb); maximum take-off 8,931kg (19,689lb)
Dimensions: span 11.1m (36.42ft); length 11.41m (37.42ft); wing area 24.15m (260sq ft)
Production: 226 aircraft

Variants include the 84C, 84D and F-84E, of which 843 were built, and finally the 84F Thunderstreak with swept flying surfaces and RF-84F Thunderflash

Saab 35X Draken

Country of origin: Sweden
Type: all-weather fighter, attack and reconnaissance aircraft
First flight: October 1955
Accommodation: pilot
Armament: two Aden 30mm cannon in the wings with 100 rounds per gun, plus up to 4,500kg (9,921lb) stores
Electronics and operational equipment: communication and navigation equipment, plus Saab S7BX weapon-delivery radar and computer system and a Saab BT9 toss-bombing computer
Powerplant and fuel system: one 8,000kg (17,650lb) afterburning thrust Volvo Flygmotor RM6C turbojet
Performance: maximum speed 2,125km/h (1,320mph) or Mach 2 at high altitude; range 635-km (395-mile) hi-lo-hi radius, or 3,250km (2,020 miles) for ferrying with maximum internal and external fuel
Weights: normal take-off 11,400kg (25,130lb); maximum take-off 16,000kg (35,275lb)
Dimensions: span 9.4m (30ft 10in); length 15.35m (50ft 4in); height 3.89m (12ft 9in); wing area 49.20m² (529.6sq ft)

Production totalled 525, and with upgrades some have continued in service into the 1990s

Saab-Scania AJ 37 Viggen

Country of origin: Sweden
Type: all-weather attack aircraft
First flight: February 1967
Accommodation: pilot
Armament (fixed): none
Armament (disposable): up to a maximum weight of 6,000kg (13,228lb)
Electronics and operational equipment: communication and navigation equipment, plus L.M. Ericsson UAP-1023 search and attack radar and Saab-Scania CK-37 central computer
Powerplant and fuel system: one 11,800kg (26,015lb) afterburning thrust Volvo Flygmotor RM8A (licence-built and modified Pratt & Whitney JT8D-22) turbofan
Performance: maximum speed 2,125km/h (1,320mph); climb to 10,000m (32,810ft) in less than 1 minute 40 seconds; range at least 1,000-km (621-mile) hi-lo-hi radius
Weights: empty about 11,800kg (26,015lb); normal take-off 15,000kg (33,069lb); maximum take-off 20,500kg (45,194lb)
Dimensions: span 10.60m (34ft 9.25in) and canard 5.45m (17ft 10.5in); length 16.30m (53ft 5.75in) including probe; height 5.80m (19ft 0.25in); wing area 46m² (495.1sq ft) and canard 6.2m² (66.74sq ft)
Production: Sweden 149

An exciting double-delta designed
aircraft

Saab-Scania JAS 39A Gripen

Country of origin: Sweden
Type: all-weather fighter
First flight: December 1988
Accommodation: pilot on a Martin-Baker S10LS zero/zero ejector seat
Armament (fixed): one 27mm Mauser BK27 cannon with an unrevealed number of rounds
Armament (disposable): carried on six hardpoints up to a maximum weight of about 6,500kg (14,330lb)
Electronics and operational equipment: communications and navigation equipment, plus Ericsson PS-05/A pulse-Doppler search and acquisition radar
Powerplant and fuel system: one 8,200kg (18,080lb) afterburning thrust Volvo Flygmotor RM12 turbofan
Performance: maximum speed about 2,125km/h (1,320mph) or Mach 2 at high altitude; initial climb rate not revealed; service ceiling not revealed; range not revealed
Weights: empty not revealed, maximum take-off 11,350kg (25,022lb)
Dimensions: span 8.0m (26ft 3in); length 14.1m (48ft 3in): height 4.7m (15ft 5in); wing area not revealed
Production: 30 aircraft

The first prototype crashed, owing to a fault in the flight control system

SEPECAT Jaguar A and S

Country of origin: France/UK
Type: close-support and reconnaissance
First flight: August 1976
Accommodation: pilot
Armament (fixed): two Aden 30mm cannon
Armament (disposable): this is carried on one underfuselage hardpoint and four underwing hardpoints, up to 4,763kg (10,500lb)
Electronics and operational equipment: communication and navigation equipment
Powerplant and fuel system: two 3,647kg (8,040lb) afterburning thrust Rolls-Royce/Turboméca Adour Mk 104 turbofans
Performance: maximum speed 1,700km/h (1,056mph) or Mach 1.6 at 11,000m (36,090ft), and 1,350km/h (840mph) or Mach 1.1 at sea-level; climb to 9,145m (30,000ft) in 1 minute 30 seconds; service ceiling 14,000m (45,930ft); range 537-km (334-mile) lo-lo-lo radius with internal fuel
Weights: empty 7,000kg (15,432lb); normal take-off 10,955kg (24,150lb); maximum take-off 15,700kg (34,612lb)
Dimensions: span 8.69m (28ft 6in); length 16.83m (55ft 2.5in) including probe; height 4.89m (16ft 0.5in); wing area 24.18m² (260.27sq ft)
Production: 608 aircraft

The Jaguar 'A' is the French variant and 'S' the UK version

Shenyang J-8-11 'Finback'

Country of origin: China
Type: air-superiority fighter with secondary ground-attack capability
First flight: 1984
Accommodation: pilot
Armament (fixed): two 30mm cannon
Armament (disposable): this is accommodated on underwing hardpoints including drop-tanks and disposable stores up to an unspecified weight
Electronics and operational equipment: communication and navigation equipment
Powerplant and fuel system: two Wopen WP-7 (Tumanskii R-11) afterburning turbojets, rated at 60.72kN (13,668lb) thrust each
Performance: maximum speed 2,500km/h (1,553mph); service ceiling 18,000m (59,055ft); range 1,850km (1,150 miles)
Weights: empty 12,000kg (26,455lb); loaded 19,000kg (41,888lb)
Dimensions: span 10.00m (32ft 9.7in); length 19.00m (62ft 4in); height 5.20m (17ft 0.7in); span 40.00m² (430.57sq ft)

Upgrades are in hand, using WP-13A-ii (R-13-300) engines, and USA electronics

Singapore Aircraft Industries A-4 Super Skyhawk

Country of origin: USA/Singapore
Type: light ground attack fighter
First flight: June 1954
Accommodation: pilot
Armament (fixed): two 30mm cannon
Armament (disposable): provision for up to 4,153kg (9,156lb) of disposable stores
Electronics and operational equipment: communications and navigation equipment
Powerplant and fuel system: one General Electric F404-GE-100D non-afterburning turbofan, rated at 48.06kN (10,800lb st) thrust
Performance: maximum speed 1,100km/h (684mph); service ceiling not available; range not available
Weights: loaded about 12,437kg (27,420lb)
Dimensions: span 8.38m (27ft 6in); length 12.29m (40ft 4in); height 4.57m (15ft 10in); wing area 24.16m² (260sq ft)

Originally built as a carrierborne fighter, a land-based variant was built and recent upgrades for South-East Asian countries have resulted in the Super Skyhawk, with greater power and modern electronics

SOKO J-22B Orao 2/CNIAR IAR-93B

Country of origin: Yugoslavia/Romania
Type: close air-support
First flight: October 1983
Accommodation: pilot on ejector seat
Armament (fixed): two 23mm GSh-23L twin barrel cannon with 200 rounds per gun
Armament (disposable): carried on five hard-points up to a maximum weight of 2,800kg (6,173lb)
Electronics and operational equipment: communications and navigation equipment
Powerplant and fuel system: two 2,268kg (5,000lb) afterburning thrust Orao/Turbomécanica-built Rolls-Royce Viper Mk 633-41 turbojets and a total internal fuel capacity of 3,100 litres (682 Imp gal)
Performance: maximum speed 1,160km/h (721mph) or Mach 0.95 at sea level; initial climb rate 4,200m (13,780ft) per minute; service ceiling 13,500m (44,290ft); radius 450km (280 miles) on a lo-lo-hi mission
Weights: empty 5,750kg (12,676lb); maximum take-off weight 11,250kg (24,802lb)
Dimensions: span 9.62m (31ft 6.75in); length 14.90m (48ft 10.6in); height 4.45m (14ft 7.25in); wing area 26m² (279.86sq ft)
Production: Romania 200, Yugoslavia 135

Simple attack fighter, using engines produced under licence by Turbomécanica

Sukhoi Su-7BMK 'Fitter-A'

Country of origin: USSR
Type: ground-attack fighter
First flight: 1955
Accommodation: pilot on an ejector seat
Armament: two NR-30 30mm cannon with 70 rounds per gun in the wing roots, plus up to a nominal weight of 2,500kg (5,511lb) of stores
Electronics and operational equipment: communication and navigation equipment, plus ranging radar in the inlet centrebody, Sirena 3 radar-warning receiver and ASP-5PF gyro sight
Powerplant and fuel system: one 10,000kg (22,046lb) afterburning thrust Lyulka AL-7F-1
Performance: maximum speed 1,700km/h (1,055mph) or Mach 1.6 at 11,000m (36,090ft), and 1,350km/h (840mph) or Mach 1.1 at sea level; initial climb rate about 9,120m (29,920ft) per minute; service ceiling 15,150m (49,700ft); range 345-km (215-mile) combat radius with two drop-tanks, or 1,450km (901 miles) for ferrying with maximum fuel
Weights: empty 8,620kg (19,004lb); normal take-off 12,000kg (26,445lb); maximum take-off 13,500kg (29,762lb)
Dimensions: span 8.93m (29ft 3.5in); length 17.37m (57ft) including probe; height 4.57m (15ft); wing area 31.5m² (339.1sq ft)

A most popular fighter, despite both limited weaponry and fuel capacity

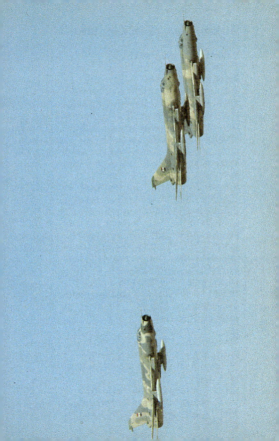

Sukhoi Su-15 'Flagon-F'

Country of origin: USSR
Type: all-weather interceptor fighter
Accommodation: pilot seated on an ejector seat
Armament (fixed): possibly one GSh-23 23mm twin-barrel cannon in the lower fuselage
Armament (disposable): this is carried on four underwing hardpoints, and generally comprises two IR-homing AA-3 'Anab' and two radar-homing AA-3-2 'Advanced Anab' air-to-air missiles
Electronics and operational equipment: communication and navigation equipment, plus 'Skip Spin' interception radar in the inlet centrebody
Powerplant and fuel system: probably two 7,200kg (15,873lb) afterburning thrust Tumanskii R-13F2-300 turbojets
Performance: maximum speed about 2,655km/h (1,650mph); climb to 11,000m (36,090ft) in 2.5 minutes; range 725-km (450-mile) combat radius
Weights: empty 12,500kg (27,557lb); normal take-off 16,000kg (35,273lb); maximum take-off 20,500kg (45,194lb)
Dimensions: span 10.53m (34ft 6in); length 20.5m (68ft); height 5m (16ft 5in); wing area 36m² (387.7sq ft)

A development of the Su-11, that

170 *entered service in the early 1960s*

Sukhoi Su-20 'Fitter-C'

Country of origin: USSR
Type: variable-geometry ground-attack
First flight: 1966
Accommodation: pilot on a KM-1 zero/zero ejector seat
Armament (fixed): two 30mm NR-30 cannon with 70 rounds per gun
Armament (disposable): carried on eight hardpoints up to a maximum weight of 4,000kg (8,818lb)
Electronics and operational equipment: communications and navigational equipment plus SRD-5M 'High Fix' ranging radar
Powerplant and fuel system: one 11,200kg (24,690lb) afterburning thrust Lyulka AL-21F-3 turbojet, and a total internal fuel capacity of 4,550 litres (1,000 Imp gal)
Performance: maximum speed 2,220km/h (1,379mph) or Mach 2.09 at 11,000m (36,090ft); initial climb rate 14,950m (49,050ft) per minute; service ceiling 18,000m (59,055ft); radius 685km (426 miles) on a hi-hi-hi mission
Weights: empty 10,000kg (22,046lb); maximum take-off 17,700kg (39,021lb)
Dimensions: span 13.8m (45ft 3in) spread, and 10m (32ft 10in) swept; length 18.75m (61ft 6.25in); height 5m (16ft 5in); wing area 40m² (430sq ft)

A further development of the
172 *classic Su-7 ground attack fighter*

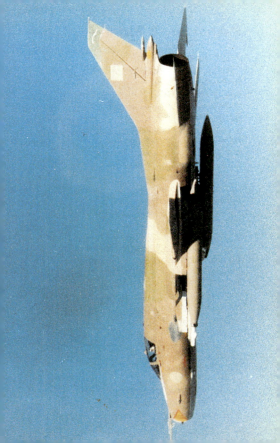

Sukhoi Su-22 'Fitter-J'

Country of origin: USSR
Type: ground attack fighter
Accommodation: pilot only, on ejector seat
Armament (fixed): two 30mm NR-30 guns
Armament (disposable): 3,175kg (7,000lb) bombs, including 'Atoll' air-to-air missiles
Electronics and operational equipment: ranging radar, ASP-5ND fire-control system and radar warning system
Powerplant and fuel system: one Tumanskii R-29B turbojet, rated at 112.8kN (25,350lb st); internal fuel tankage 6,270 litres (1,379 Imp gal)
Performance: maximum speed 2,230km/h (1,380mph) or Mach 2.09 at high altitude; climb rate 13,800m (45,275ft) per minute; service ceiling 18,000m (59,050ft)
Weights: empty 10,000kg (22,046lb); maximum take-off 17,700kg (39,020lb)
Dimensions: span 13.8m (45ft 3in) spread and 10m (32ft 10in) swept; length 18.75m (61ft 6.25in) including probes; height 5m (16ft 5in); wing area 40m² (430sq ft)
Production: The Su-22 was also supplied to the Libyan Air Force and is a derivative of the Sukhoi Su-17, Su-20 'Fitter' series, which was first shown in July 1967 at the Soviet Aviation Day display

A 'Fitter-G' comes in to land with the variable-geometry wings fully forward

174

Sukhoi Su-24 'Fencer-C'

Country of origin: USSR
Type: variable-geometry attack and interdiction
Entered service: 1974
Accommodation: pilot and weapons officer
Armament: possibly one GSh-23 23mm twin-barrel cannon under the port side of the fuselage, plus maximum load of 8,000kg (17,635lb)
Electronics and operational equipment: communication and navigation equipment, plus attack and navigation radars, radar-warning receiver and other systems including terrain-avoidance radar
Powerplant and fuel system: probably two 11,200kg (24,691lb) afterburning thrust Lyulka AL-21F-3
Performance: maximum speed more than 2,125km/h (1,320mph) or Mach 2 at high altitude; service ceiling 17,500m (57,415ft); range 1,800-km (1,115-mile) hi-lo-hi radius with 2,000kg (4,409lb) payload and two external tanks
Weights: maximum take-off 39,500kg (87,081lb)
Dimensions: span 17.15m (56ft 3in) spread and 9.53m (31ft 3in) swept; length 21.29m (69ft 10in); height 5.5m (18ft); wing area about 40m² (430.5sq ft)
Production: 912 aircraft

The Soviets' first true variable-geometry aircraft to enter service

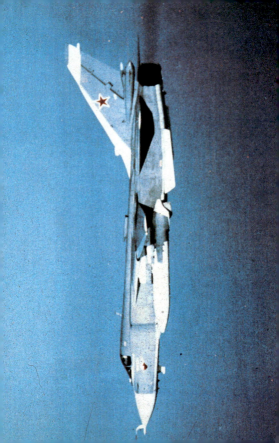

Sukhoi Su-25K 'Frogfoot-C'

Country of origin: USSR
Type: close air-support
First flight: 1980
Accommodation: pilot on an ejector seat
Armament (fixed): one 30mm twin-barrel cannon with 250 rounds
Armament (disposable): carried on ten hardpoints up to a maximum weight of 4,500kg (9,921lb)
Electronics and operational equipment: communications and navigation equipment
Powerplant and fuel system: two 4,500kg (9,921lb) thrust Tumanskii R-195 non-afterburning turbojets and a total internal fuel weight of about 5,000kg (11,023lb)
Performance: maximum speed 850km/h (528mph) at optimum altitude; initial climb rate not revealed; service ceiling 7,000m (22,965ft); radius 550km (342 miles) with a 4,000kg (8,818lb) warload
Weights: empty 9,500kg (20,944lb); maximum take-off 17,600kg (38,801lb)
Dimensions: span 14.36m (47ft 1.4in); length 15.55m (51ft 0.2in); height not revealed; wing area 37.6m² (404.74sq ft)
Production: 455 aircraft

Produced as a counterpart to the Fairchild Republic A-10A Thunderbolt II: early craft were pressed into service in Afghanistan

Sukhoi Su-27 'Flanker-B'

Country of origin: USSR
Type: air-superiority fighter
Entered service: 1986
Accommodation: pilot on a KM-1 zero/zero ejector seat
Armament (fixed): one 30mm six-barrel rotary cannon
Armament (disposable): carried on ten hardpoints up to about 6,000kg (13,228lb) of missiles and free-fall ordnance
Electronics and operational equipment: communications and navigation equipment, plus 'Flash Dance' pulse-Doppler nose radar
Powerplant and fuel system: two 13,600kg (29,982lb) afterburning thrust Lyulka AL-31F turbofans and a total internal fuel weight of about 7,000kg (15,432lb)
Performance: maximum speed 2,495km/h (1,550mph) or Mach 2.35 at high altitude; initial climb rate 18,300m (60,040ft) per minute; service ceiling 15,000m (49,215ft); radius 1,500km (932 miles) with four AAMs
Weights: empty 17,700kg (39,021lb); maximum take-off 30,000kg (66,138lb)
Dimensions: span 14.7m (48ft 2.75in); length 21.9m (71ft 10.2in); height 5.5m (18ft 0.5in); wing area 46.5m² (500.5sq ft)

The Su-27 has a fixed wing, rather than a variable-geometry configuration as was once thought

Supermarine Scimitar F.Mk 1

Country of origin: UK
Type: carrierborne strike fighter
First flight: January 1956
Accommodation: pilot
Armament (fixed): four 30mm cannon
Armament (disposable): up to 1,814kg (4,000lb) of weapons including nuclear ordnance
Electronics and operational equipment: communications and navigation equipment
Powerplant: two 5,103kgp (11,250lb) Rolls-Royce Avon 202 turbojets
Performance: maximum speed 1,186km/h (640kt) or Mach 0.968 at sea level; service ceiling 14,020m (46,000ft); range 2,288km (1,134 naut miles)
Weights: empty 10,869kg (23,962lb); maximum take-off 15,513kg (34,200lb)
Dimensions: span 11.3m (37.16ft); length 16.85m (55.25ft); wing area 45.05m² (484.9sq ft)
Production: 76 aircraft

Designed as nuclear-capable fighters, these were replaced by the Blackburn Buccaneers from 1969

Vought A-7E Corsair II

Country of origin: USA
Type: shipboard attack aircraft and tactical fighter
Entered service: 1966
Accommodation: pilot seated on a McDonnell Douglas Escapac ejector seat
Armament: one General Electric M61A1 Vulcan rotary-barrel 20mm cannon with 1,000 rounds in the port side of the fuselage, plus maximum stores of 6,804kg (15,000lb)
Electronics and operational equipment: communication and navigation equipment
Powerplant and fuel system: one 6,804kg (15,000lb) thrust Allison TF41-A-2 (licence-built Rolls-Royce Spey) turbofan
Performance: maximum speed 1,110km/h (690mph) or Mach 0.9 at sea level, and 1,038km/h (645mph) or Mach 0.86 at 1,525m (5,000ft) with 12 Mk 82 227kg (500lb) bombs; range 3,669km (2,280 miles) on internal fuel, and 4,603km (2,860 miles) with maximum internal and external fuel
Weights: empty 8,676kg (19,127lb); maximum take-off 19,050kg (42,000lb)
Dimensions: span 11.8m (38ft 9in); length 14.06m (46ft 1.5in); height 4.9m (16ft.75in); wing area 34.83m² (375sq ft)
Aircraft in service: USA 380+

The type first entered service as the
A-7A: right is the A-7E Corsair II

Vought F-8E Crusader

Country of origin: USA
Type: shipboard fighter
First flight: March 1955
Accommodation: pilot on an ejector seat
Armament (fixed): four Colt-Browning M39 20mm cannon with 144 rounds per gun
Armament (disposable): this is carried on the fuselage sides (four AIM-9 Sidewinder air-to-air missiles or eight 127mm [5in] rockets) and on two underwing hardpoints, up to a maximum weight of 2,268kg (5,000lb)
Electronics and operational equipment: communication and navigation equipment, plus AN/APQ-94 search and fire-control radar
Powerplant and fuel system: one 8,165kg (18,000lb) afterburning thrust Pratt & Whitney J57-P-20 turbojet
Performance: maximum speed 1,827km/h (1,135mph); service ceiling 17,680m (58,000ft); range 966-km (600-mile) combat radius
Weights: normal take-off 12,700kg (28,000lb); maximum take-off 15,420kg (34,000lb)
Dimensions: span 10.87m (35ft 8in); length 16.61m (54ft 6in); height 4.80m (15ft 9in); wing area 32.52m² (350sq ft)

The variable-incidence wing enables the fuselage to be kept level during take-off and landing

Yakovlev Yak-36MP 'Forger-A'

Country of origin: USSR
Type: shipboard VTOL combat aircraft
Accommodation: pilot seated on an ejector seat
Armament (fixed): none
Armament (disposable): this is carried on four underwing hardpoints, up to a maximum weight of about 1,360kg (3,000lb)
Electronics and operational equipment: communication and navigation equipment, plus ranging radar
Powerplant and fuel system: one vectored-thrust turbojet in the rear fuselage, with a rating of about 7,950kg (17,526lb) thrust, and two direct-lift Kolesov turbojets in the forward fuselage, each with a rating of about 3,625kg (7,992lb) thrust
Performance: maximum speed 1,170km/h (725mph); initial climb rate 4,500m (14,765ft) per minute; service ceiling 12,000m (39,370ft); range 370-km (230-mile) hi-lo-hi radius with maximum weapon load
Weights: empty 7,465kg (16,500lb); maximum take-off 11,565kg (25,495lb)
Dimensions: span 7.32m (24ft); length 15.25m (50ft); height 4.37m (14ft 4in); wing area 16m² (172.22sq ft)

Lightly armed, the Yak-36 was used as an experimental version of the Yak-38

Yakovlev Yak-38 'Forger-A'

Country of origin: USSR
Type: shipboard STOVL strike fighter
Entered service: 1976
Accommodation: pilot
Armament (fixed): none
Armament (disposable): provision for two medium-range air-to-air missiles up to a maximum weight of 3,600kg (7,937lb)
Electronics and operational equipment: communications and navigation equipment
Powerplant and fuel system: one 8,200kgp (18,078lb) Lyulka vectored thrust turbofan and two 4,100kgp (9,039lb) Kolesov lift turbojets
Performance: maximum speed 1,164km/h (657mph); service ceiling 12,000m (39,370ft); range 240-km (150-mile) radius on a lo-lo-lo mission with maximum load
Weights: empty 7,385kg (16,281lb); loaded 13,000kg (28,660lb)
Dimensions: span 7.32m (24ft 0.2in); length 15.50m (50ft 10.3in); height 4.37m (14ft 4in); wing area 18.50m² (199.14sq ft)
Production: 75 aircraft

Yak-38s aboard a Kiev class Soviet aircraft carrier

Abbreviations and Glossary

Clean: in-flight configuration with all landing gear retracted

ehp: equivalent horsepower, made up of shp plus addition due to residual thrust from jet

Fly-by-wire: flight control system with electrical rather than mechanical controls

kt: knot, one nautical mile per hour

kW: kilowatt, SI measure of all forms of power

lb st: non-SI measurement of static thrust

naut miles: a nautical mile is 1.8532km, or 1.15152 miles

Radius: the return flight distance from base without making an intermediate landing

Recce: reconnaissance

Service ceiling: usually the height equivalent to air density at which maximum attainable rate of climb is 100ft/min

shp: power transmitted via rotating shaft

STOL: short take-off and landing

Turbofan: gas-turbine jet engine generating most thrust by a large-diameter cowled fan, with a small part added by jet from core

Turbojet: simplest form of gas turbine, comprising compressor, combustion chamber, turbine and propulsive nozzle

Turboprop: gas turbine in which as much energy as possible is taken from gas jet and used to drive reduction gearbox and propeller

Wing area: includes all control surfaces and area of fuselage bounded by leading and trailing edges projected to centreline.